TIME FOR EACH OTHER

By MARGARET LEE RUNBECK

OUR MISS BOO
FOR TODAY ONLY
THE GREAT ANSWER
TIME FOR EACH OTHER

Time for Each Other

by

MARGARET LEE RUNBECK

Author of OUR MISS BOO

D. Appleton-Century Company

INCORPORATED

New York   London

TO MY
FATHER AND MOTHER
who taught by being

Contents

CONTENTS

TIME FOR EACH OTHER

I

A Life Worth Saving

A STRANGE THING has happened to our house during the last year. But no stranger, probably, than what has happened to yours.

A house must have four sides, no matter what its shape or its size. A house must have hands clasped at the joints of its walls, to hold them together. There must be a pair of strong hands, and a pair of smaller but even stronger ones, and then, of course, there are the children, and the pets, and whatever else lives within the walls.

In our house there is only one child ... our Miss Boo; only one statistically, that is. But of course there are countless other children of longer or shorter duration, for we live in the country, and a country house is nothing without its guests.

If I counted up the number of noses which normally dwell here, they would run into scores. But some of them are the furry noses of teddy bears, and the complacent little tweaky noses of the dolls, and the trunk of Ella, who is made of gray and cerise velvet with white satin tusks. Then there is the chocolate nose of Lilliam, who came to us out of the night a few years ago, and has stayed, and has braided her life into ours so that it can never be untangled, we hope.

"Seems lak I never did live anywheres else," Lilliam says. When she tries to remember her life before she came to our house, it blurs into folklore. "Seems lak I was born in Georgia, but then again seems lak I was born in Vaginger. One thing I do know," she says confidently, "I *was* born. Sure enough."

Like a play within a play, Lilliam's family lives within our family. Only her family, too, has had that thing happen to it this year. For Joseph also has gone to war.

So now you know what it is that has happened to our house. One of its walls—its strongest, highest wall, has been taken away. We are only a three-walled house now. It has opened us out from ourselves, having this most important wall of ours be far away. The world lies between us now. Sometimes at night when I go out alone and walk along our country road, and then look back upon our lighted house, solid and strong among its trees, I think about this, and it seems to me our whole house has become, not smaller as you might expect with Peter away for a year now, but larger. For the whole world is between it and its outermost wall. Wherever Peter is to-night as I write this . . . and I do not know exactly where, as you may not know where your own man is . . . I know that place is the boundary of this home of ours.

"How high does it extend?" I used to ask him when we first bought our land.

"To the skies," he said. "Stars on the rooftree belong to us. Says so in the deed."

"Wherever you are, there is my home," we said to each other. Just as you, too, must have said it.

I used to want us to be close, bounded on all sides by what belonged to us, our books and the family jokes and the people we loved, our child and her jostling world of make-believe and reality. I wanted us self-contained, as women always do who love their own. Safe and centered, I wanted us. I loved the world, but I kept it separate, beyond the sweet circumference of this home, and us.

There was everything else, and there was us, and that was how I wanted it to be. Our share of the world, I called it to myself, and many a morning in my garden I stopped weeding a while and thought: "I'd like to give mornings like this to every one on earth. . . ." And many a twilight, when baths were running and Peter was whistling and Lilliam downstairs was weaving silently back and forth from kitchen to dining-room, from oven to pantry, I thought: "Dear God, give a piece of this to all the lonely ones on earth."

When I looked into the merry eyes of our Miss Boo, blue as heaven, and flecked by questions, I thought, "Give every house its child, God. . . ."

But something has happened to my share of the world now; it has become both smaller and larger. Nothing belongs to us alone any more. The sorrow and the toil, the uncertainty and the quick, unbearable delight, belong to all of us together now.

While Peter is gone, we keep our life intact for him. We want him to come back and find that what he has been fighting for has been worth saving. Every one in our neighborhood is putting up things, and I "put up things," too, for Peter to have when he returns. Tomatoes and beans and peaches and grape juice, we are all storing away in our cellars against leaner days to come.

"These'll taste mighty good, come winter," we say, looking at our jewels lined along shelves. We feel a little shiver of drama when we look at them, and wonder what will be the texture of that day, not so many months from now, when we open those jars. Days, even a few months from now, are mysterious and unguessable, for the world is changing faster than we know.

I do my canning with the rest of the neighbors, the heavy grapes, sun-warmed and drowsy, the corn so exhausting to the knife-thumb, and the ubiquitous tomatoes. But mostly what I "put up" won't go into any Mason jar, hot pack or cold pack. Mostly I want to preserve these days of ours, to be opened and tasted later in our lifetime, when Peter is home again. Some winter evening when Miss Boo is away at Vassar I want to go down into our dark cellar and, holding up my flashlight, see these days standing along the shelf, colorful and gemlike with their flavor, the spiced, the minty, and the bitter, all sealed in. I can see my Peter cocking his head, while he tastes these days when we were apart. . . .

There'd be a rainy day with the fire for a heart, and Miss Boo learning to play checkers (and me, after a lifetime of looking, at last finding some one I can beat). There'd be picnic days ("But why call it a 'family get-together' . . . it's a 'be-together' isn't it?" Boo said seriously). There'd be the high blue windy day we made the kite, and the other day we found the turtle, and the day the bunny, no bigger than one's hand, came and was loved and looked at all afternoon in a wastebasket (and the other day when his mothers and fathers and uncles and aunts returned to thank us, and stripped our cabbages as they left).

The important days I'll remember without trying; nothing could ever take them. But the ordinary days, the dear usual ones, so plentiful they can be wasted now in wishing they were over . . . these are the ones I must preserve, for all of us.

These days, which used old-fashionedly to be called "the best years of our life," millions of us in this country and across the world are living apart! So while we must live them apart, let us keep them for each other.

That's what I am trying to do in this book. I am doing it for Peter, of course, and for myself. But also I am doing it for you, for I hope that when you sample mine, you'll find preserved along with them days of your own, ordinary dear days, salty, or spiced, or sweet.

It is not difficult for me to keep our house happy these days, for we have Miss Boo. That taut sky of worry, which stretches over all of us who have men away from home, is there of course. But sometimes . . . most of the time . . . I can keep from looking at it. I can live in the lovely now, as a child does, regretting nothing that is past, fearing nothing that is ahead. I think it is the formula for getting through these days, when we have working to do with our hands, and hoping to do with our hearts.

In this interim, there are many of us women and children who have achieved a strange spurious happiness. A determined brave happiness, if you will. We dare not look at it very closely, or we should see how heartbroken it really is.. . .

But it has its purposes, and they are good ones. For there is a world to be held together, and we, the un-regimented hostages who wait and work, are the ones who must do the holding.

Miss Boo is eight now; that is what the statistics say about her. But sometimes she is still only four, and needing to sit on my lap, and sometimes she is a con-temporary of God Himself, old as wisdom.

I look at her and try to find traces of the children she has been, and sometimes I see fleeting footprints of all those children who have come and gone in her. She was a sassy-looking baby who never would lie down properly like a Madonna's infant but wanted to sit bolt upright on your knee, looking alert for a good racy bit of gossip. She was half-bunny and half-pixie; then, gradually, she became all doll, with golden ring-lets and a tooth. Only a month or so ago, it seems to me, she was four, and then six, and now she can read. She can sound out any word and pronounce it accu-rately, through a handy little book called succinctly *Word Mastery*. She practically holds her nose when she thinks of this book, but it has performed miracles. No word, however long, is safe from her now. She pro-nounces it perfectly, and she usually adds, "Whatever *that* means." Lilliam looks on in incredulity, and some-times she says, "Jes lemme see that, Doll Baby," and Boo shows it to her, and Lilliam shakes her head. For letters and words remain the ultimate mystery of the world to her.

Lilliam has her own way of reading, when she must

read. She knows the shape of words, without benefit of letters. She can read recipes and the Bible, and that covers all her needs.

The walls of our house ... and of any house ... are the covers of a book. The book is wide open now, for the world has moved into our story, and we can not tell how wide it will be. We can not tell, any of us these days, how the pages will fall between the front cover, which bears the unwritten title of our life, and the back cover. There was a time when you could look at lives and know what they held, but now there are cottages and tenements and mansions all over our land that have Africa and Italy and Japan written into them.

Stars still twinkle on our rooftrees; and equally wide the outermost walls of all our houses have been pushed out to include the world.

II

Sincerest Form of Buffoonery

I᠇ isn't difficult to be happy in our house, even our three-walled one, for a house with a child in it has laughter shining out of it like candlelight from a jack-o'-lantern.

If you want a cartoon of yourself, watch your children playing. They are satirists without venom, so gentle that you can not resent, so sincere that their imitation is flattery rather than ridicule. They imitate and burlesque, and if they weren't so utterly innocent about it, we'd have to spank 'em for impudence. Nobody has any right to understand us the way our children do, our whining voices, our pretentious vanities, and our wistfully preposterous make-believes. They pick out our most comical characteristics and dramatize them, and when you hear them giving their incisive stage directions to each other before the play begins, you sometimes blush for shame, recognizing yourself.

"Make believe I'm trying to get you to clean house, and you don't know it," they say. "Make believe I'm pretending it's going to be fun for you."

I have in my possession a lot of embarrassing information about my friends, picked up from overhearing their children playing with our Miss Boo. The uncomfortable corollary of that is that I know they know all about me, too.

There's one child whose mother and father are the examples of connubial sugar-and-cream for the rest of the town. But their child always plays house in a monologue of nagging.

"Make believe you're the father, and I'm the mother. You must want to leave your coat in the hall, and I must make you take it upstairs. You must want to lie out in the hammock, and I must make you wash windows." On and on it goes, while the other child stands around stupefied, giving, no doubt, a truer impersonation of the "father" than they actually realize.

There are children to whom pretending to be grown up means quarreling about money or gossiping scandalously. One of the most pathetic children of all who come to our house is little Elaine, who always wants to be the mother, and whose principal household activity is to punish her children.

"Make out you've been bad all day, and now I'm going to spank you," she says gluttonously. "I'm going to give you a scolding and then a good sound spanking. I'm going to put you to bed without any supper."

They agree unenthusiastically, and Elaine, in a sadistic orgy, carries out her devotions solemnly. You see, she has a progressive mother who doesn't believe in punishing children. She just lets 'em think things over, and goodness knows there's no fun in *that*.

One child, a chubby-cheeked Amazon, always wants to "play medicine."

"Make believe you're coming over to my house to

tea," Miss Boo says hopefully when they're deciding what to play.

"If I'm well enough," Alice says. "Make believe I've had a cold all week, and I'm in bed with the doctor."

"All right. But you get up and come over after the doctor leaves."

All this is executed at length, and finally Alice, clad in a very thin nightgown of voice, arrives for tea, dragging her ailments behind her like a bedraggled train.

"I don't feel at all well," she says in aching syllables.

Boo, who considers ill-health a kind of tedious affectation, tries politely to throw Alice her cues. After all, Boo is the hostess, and heaven knows you've got to be polite.

"What seems to be the matter, darling?" she says animatedly.

"Oh, just a slight touch of change of life," Alice says in a patient whimper. "My husband had it last week, and I must have caught it from him."

III

Cukey

THE life of a house runs along almost like music, an undertone you're conscious of without really listening to it. Life in any house is written like melody along the staff of the days, and each member, the whole notes and the sixteenths, contributes his part to the song. Some days, no matter what you do to quiet it, there is martial music, rampant and brassy; sometimes there is popular-song banality, all the "Junes," so to speak, inanely rhyming with "moons." On the days you clean the attic, or make chili sauce, there are unexpected folksongs in a house.

Sometimes you are appalled because your family adds up only to juke-box trash, without charm or character, and then, for a few brief moments—just at twilight, perhaps, or early in the morning before the commonplace strides into right of way—family-music rises into the nobility of a Psalm, and your house is a harp, touched by the hand of God.

We have the usual orchestrations in our house, ranging from the heavy and somber to prankish, merry-go-round, calliope music. But whatever tempo is written, there are always grace notes, little black grace notes, rippling off the edges of the days. The grace notes are Cukey.

11

Cukey is only eight months old; before we got him he shined shoes, sold newspapers, and ran errands for the angels in heaven. That's what Lilliam says. She knows, too, because Cukey told her so. Cukey tells her a mess of stuff, outrageous and profound.

Lilliam stands before me, with her good black hands folded meekly into her white apron, and her dark, beautiful face quite serious, while she tells me things that Cukey tells her.

Lilliam puts over many a smooth deal in our house in Cukey's name. Many a sly cargo comes into our port convoyed by the innocent wishes of Cukey.

"Cukey say he gotta have more butter, efn I'se gwine bake pie," she says, looking steadfastly at me. "Cukey say you hafta give up table butter for lunch, efn us gwine eat pie. Fum now *awn,* Cukey say."

Or even bolder: "Cukey say his momma need that little pink hat you use' wear last spring. Cukey say you bettah have nice new hat, Missy. No use you wearin' any ole pink hat. . . ."

If you came into our kitchen and saw him tied in his red high chair to keep him from spreading his invisible wings and flying out of the window, you couldn't help saying to yourself, "That's what this kitchen always needed! How did we ever keep house without Cukey?"

He sits there, with his double-bubble cheeks sunk in his starched frill of a chest, and his eyes, black and polished, tiptoeing around the kitchen, watching everything Lilliam does. He's as solemn and as bland as a baby Buddha . . . not an expensive one, but one of those plastics stamped into the shape of incense burners.

Cukey is, in fact, a kind of incense burner, sitting in his red high chair, while the fragrance of his contentment and the pungency of his mirth pervade the whole house.

Whatever routine cerebration he achieves later in life, right now he's a philosopher and a sage; right now you feel as if you ought to bend the knee and ask his advice humbly. Cukey at eight months is the most thoughtful-looking deity that ever answered petition with silence, or pleading with a grin.

Sometimes, when you're trying to be ingratiating, he regards you steadily and then closes his eyes wearily, and you feel yourself blushing from the soles of your feet with failure. No matter how you exert yourself, he is definitely not amused. If he has thinking to do, he slumps more solidly on his digestive apparatus and lets his brain simmer in silence.

At other times, he is delirious with your skill as an entertainer. He flashes those two far-apart teeth of his and waves his mocha fist in your face and doubles over with mirth at your cleverness. And you are absurdly pleased.

Joseph, Cukey's father, our fine silent grass-cutter and car-driver and general muscle-man, is constantly present by his absence. We miss him terribly, though we have little grass to cut now that the vegetables have marched belligerently upon us, and of course we have no car-driving to do. We manage, in a way, and we have calluses on our palms which used to be on his. Besides the calluses, he left us Cukey to remember him by. Cukey is all right, but he's not the man Joseph was, by any means.

"Cukey gwine look jes lak his Daddy," Lilliam says loyally. "He favor him right smart, don' you think?"

"I don't know how you can possibly tell at this point," I say realistically, to tease her. "Right now he favors a nice chocolate Easter bunny."

"Um-*hum* he favor Joseph. He got flannel ears, jes like Joseph, and he bat his eyes when he smile."

"You bat *your* eyes," I say to her. "That's how I can tell when you're trying to get the best of me ... when you look good and innocent."

"Yas'm," she says, and smiles and bats.

Joseph has never seen Cukey, except in snapshots. They're not good snapshots; you might as well try to photograph a genie rising up out of the bottle. There are the mellow caramel cheeks and the big eyes which dart like polliwogs around their milky fishbowls. There are the licorice curls, which look as if Lilliam had fluted them on with her pastry bag. But that isn't Cukey; Cukey is something that eludes a lens. To convey Cukey, you'd have to know how to snap a giggle or a wink, or the toppling over on his face and the lying there with his blunt bottom wagging like a puppy's tail, while he gurgles in glee.

In addition to his flannel ears, Joseph gave him his name.

"Cukey was Joseph's *good* uncle," Lilliam explained when the instructions came from Missouri, where Joseph was then in camp. "Joseph thinks it's on-lucky not to name your first chile for some kinfolks. Cukey was the *good* uncle."

"Whyn't you name him after Joseph himself?" I suggested, not knowing how to spell Cukey and hoping to avoid that tussle. "Joseph is kinfolks . . . his best kinfolk next to you, Lilliam."

She looked demure then. "No'm. When he went away Joseph say he want me to keep that name jes for him. Don't want me using it common for any tongue-spanking, the way a momma's bound to haf to some-times, efn she got a little bittie boy.

"Joseph say he don' ever want to be lying down takin' his rest and hearin' me say, 'Joseph, fetch me in some wood, 'fore I smack you good. . . .' He say when he hear 'Joseph' he want it to mean him and no mis-take." Then she looked at me with the full blaze of that love of hers shining out of her eyes, and said so softly I realized she was giving me something that was precious to her: "Joseph jes want to be my on'y Joseph."

So Cukey was the name.

The middle name was Lilliam's gift to her son. It is Epworth.

"Seems lak a chile ought to have a kind of dress-up name in the middle," she said. "Give him somethin' to live up to, efn he feels shiftless an' raggy-boned. Chile say to hisse'f, 'Person name of Cukey Epworth jes got to *be* somethin'.'"

Right now, however, Cukey is pretty unconcerned about being anything. He's just tickled to pieces with the whole universe, and he likes white meat of chicken, and he gets it.

Lilliam herself never tasted white meat in her life until she was twenty-nine years old, and then it was by an accident. Even now, she can not swallow it com-fortably for the guilt that chokes her at the thought.

But Cukey is different. Cukey is her son, and his world is going to be created in the image and likeness of all the things she has never had. He's going to take for granted the things she has wanted haggardly and never quite got her fingers on. He won't realize it, of course; he'll snatch and swallow as he snatches and swallows the white meat now, hardly tasting it. But that is the way each generation goes ahead, preëmpting privileges and calling them rights. Snatching the best, the almost-out-of-reach, and trampling it underfoot unnoticed, reaching hungrily ahead.

Lilliam, suspecting not at all that this is an ancient pattern of progress, thinks it shows some unique superiority in Cukey.

"Cukey puff-furs white meat," she says with queenly dignity. And that settles it.

IV

Annabelle

THEY are their own best salesmen. The whole race of them are so pleased with themselves that they can't imagine how any one could resist having dozens of children, if it were possible. From under their spell, I too am persuaded that nothing improves most adults so much as to be surrounded on three sides by children. The fourth side is the stronghold of defended privacy. The more fiercely that is guarded, the better companion one becomes on the other fronts.

Miss Boo's idea of Utopia is a child in every house. I don't go as far as that . . . perhaps I'd settle for a child in every heart.

Sometimes it's definitely embarrassing, this constant, vigilant proselytizing she does among our friends, particularly among the unmarried or otherwise childless.

Once when a very complacent career woman was having tea with us, Miss Boo came tiptoeing in and asked me in a whisper if she couldn't "give her a present to take home."

"Why, of course, darling," I said. "You mean you have something you've picked out to give her?"

"No. But I'll find something," she said. "I just want her to have *something*."

She went upstairs, and I heard her running around

looking, snatching open drawers, rummaging in closets, and shoving things around in the attic. And muttering to herself.

At last she had it, and she brought it downstairs wrapped lumpily. I didn't inquire what it was; it looked like a loaf of bread, or my next winter's over-shoes.

After the guest had departed with the gift, I said: "That was a nice idea, dear. What did you give her?"

"My funnies. The ones you don't want me to read." They are treasures, utter treasures, being forbidden, so I was surprised indeed.

"But how did you happen to want to give her a gift?"

"Why, the poor lady," she said tremulously, "she hasn't any children."

I, of course, am the most fortunate "lady" Boo knows. I have her, and she is just the size to fit on my lap and just the shape to creep into that place under my desk where paper clips try to hide. She is somebody who can cherish my old perfume bottles, and who can dress up in my old hats and occasionally in my new ones. What would we do with the last pinch of pie dough, if Lilliam didn't have her to bake it for in a little bittie pan, not much bigger than a button? Who would remind us to pop popcorn on a Sunday afternoon when Peter and I could otherwise just idly read the books we never have time for? And for whom would we make a snow man if we didn't have a child? Who would keep a scrap book with us, sniffing the library paste as if it were attar of roses?

In fact (though this she never develops), *where* would we get those darling little star-shaped smudges on the white doors? How would we ever decide to have the furniture reupholstered, and how would we break dishes so that exciting new ones could come into our lives? We'd stagnate, you see; or worse, we'd grow up incurably.

So, knowing all this, Miss Boo quite often suggests to all and sundry that they have a few children. When she *is* reticent about some of our friends, she intends it as no compliment.

"I hope *they* never have any children," she says confidentially. "Children wouldn't like 'em. There are too many things they wouldn't have in common."

Brides and grooms especially are her meat. She'd like to get them started right from the very first week, with a full-sized baby to take on the wedding trip.

"Then they'd never be all alone," she says sympathetically.

Our dearest friends are Tom and Lisa King, who came here from Illinois when Tom became an instructor at Harvard three years ago. From the first time she saw them, Boo worked on them doggedly.

Peter and Tom have been friends since they were boys, and naturally the Kings were looking forward to knowing our Boo. They had sent her gifts, and she had laboriously written them letters. But the first time they all met, Miss Boo bluntly put her worst foot forward.

She was only five then, so she made a demure little curtsy, and then she said, "Why didn't you bring Annabelle?"

"Annabelle?"

"Yes. Your little girl."

Lisa King, who had knelt swiftly on the floor so that

she and Boo could be on a level, got up gracefully, and by the way she blushed I knew Boo had said something that was not going to be amusing.

"But we haven't any little girl, Miss Boo," Lisa said, as graciously as she could.

"You ought to have," she said, frank as a sexagenarian.

Tom King had a look on his face I shall never forget. The room was uncomfortably still, and then Peter, from his wealth of experience with an untactful daughter, plunged into economics.

But the next time Boo saw them, it was the same thing.

"Haven't you got Annabelle yet?"

Lisa was ready for her now. "No, we haven't," she said, quite composedly. "And we aren't going to have, my fine electioneering friend."

"Well, where *is* she?" Miss Boo asked, quite distressed.

Then Tom himself took over the conversation. It was he who went down on the floor this time, so they could see eye to eye.

"Annabelle's been detained," he said. "Her mother's a very busy woman."

"Oh, but children are no trouble at *all!*" Boo said. "The thing is, if you have two of them, they just take care of each other."

When Christmas came, and she dictated her list for cards, she went through her playmates, and then she said, "And of course Annabelle."

"Annabelle who?"

"Why, King, of course," she said matter-of-factly.

"But dear . . . she isn't here yet."

"All right," she said resignedly. She was quiet a long time, and I could see she was thinking carefully over Lisa and Tom, considering them from every angle as parent-material. Then she sighed regretfully. "I wish and wish she was here," she said earnestly.

Unexpectedly, Peter took charge.

"Okay, we'll tell her so," Peter said somewhat grimly. He found a Christmas card and wrote it for Miss Boo, and I couldn't do anything about it. The card said:

> *Dear Annabelle: Having a lovely time.*
> *Wish you were here.*
>
> > > *Boo.*

It took us two years to get an answer to that card. Two rather strange years, in which we all lost the vision of Lisa as a mother, and thought we must have been wrong.

For Lisa, with her lovely face and hair which seem made for footlights, wanted to be an actress more than anything else on earth.

"But she doesn't look like an actress," Miss Boo said rebelliously when I told her that Lisa had gone to New York to act in a play. "She looks like a mother."

With her sentimental prejudice, Boo was wrong about Lisa. She really did look like an actress when we saw her on a New York stage. Tom was quite proud of her, even though her part wasn't very big. He took us all to supper afterward. Peter was in his new uniform then, and a couple of young naval fliers who'd been in one of Tom's classes also came to the party. It was all very gay, and Lisa was beautiful and happy.

Peter was glum about it, when we got back to our hotel.

"Looks as if Annabelle hasn't a ghost of a chance," he said, but I just yawned and pretended I didn't know what he meant.

But the play wasn't very good, and it closed in a few weeks. Tom stopped being a haggard-looking waif, beginning to hurry on Monday morning so he could catch the train to New York on Friday afternoon. Lisa came back to Cambridge and settled down again in their beautiful old Brattle Street apartment.

"Now they'll have Annabelle," Boo said incorrigibly.

"Please, dear," I warned her. "Please don't mention it to them. They're not amused with Annabelle."

"They'll be amused later," she said confidently.

Before she had a chance to bring up the subject, Lisa had flown off again. A much better play this time, and she with a wonderful part. Suicide, and everything, she told me excitedly, over the phone.

"Did you discuss about Annabelle?" Boo wanted to know, as soon as I had hung up.

Peter looked at me and grinned.

"You go out and play," I said sternly. "You and your one-track-minded father!"

V

A Valentine

T<small>HIS</small> morning I sent Peter some pictures of Miss Boo. I know how maddeningly meager they will be to him, and yet how provocative. As I send them to him, swift pictures of him looking at them come back to me, instantaneous round trip. I see him in the terribly bright sun of Africa, standing in some quiet place so he can open the letter. (He'll carry it all day unopened, if necessary, until he can find the right place to read it; that I know about him! He'll not snatch it open and devour it as I should.)

He'll try to see her puckish apple-blossom face below the soft scribble of yellow curls. In the shadowy smudge, he will find her quick grace, and Boo will get up from the rock she is sitting on, and take him down into the woods, and show him something invisible hiding under a leaf. She'll run and jump on him, as she does, pretending to be three puppies, and he'll put her up on his shoulder ... and then both he and I will remember that she is too big to be put up on shoulders this year. She *is* too big, but he'll put her up anyway, for this is only a heartbreakingly impossible dream we are having together, with tenses mixed up and geography crumpled conveniently as you might crumple a map.

After I have the snapshots all sealed, I open the en-

velop again. For I must look at Boo's face with a mag-
nifying glass, as he will look at it. I take as long as I
possibly can over this, and I do not need to explain that
to you, for you, too, must know the desolate comfort
there is in handling the paper and string he is going to
touch. It is forlorn comfort, but it is comfort. . . .

While I was sealing it all up again, I remembered
something of long ago, when Boo was a very little baby.

"Do you think she's a beautiful child?" Peter said,
and he had on a sheepish smile. "Of course, mere beauty
isn't anything. It's character and all that stuff that
counts."

"Of course she's beautiful," I admitted.

"No. I mean it. She looks beautiful to me, but of
course I can't really tell."

"I want her to be beautiful," I said. "Inside and out."

"You'll take care of that, won't you? Teach her all
that junk about hair and skin? Maybe we ought to
begin right away. . . ."

"I have begun right away," I said. "I brush her hair."

"You do!" he said delightedly. He looked down at it
and touched her head with his finger. "It's wonderful-
looking hair," he said. "For such a little baby, of
course."

Later—two or three months later—we had a photograph taken of her. One of those big, important-looking
pictures you never show to anybody but yourselves.

"Her hair looks pretty thick," Peter said. "To tell
you the truth, I think the photographer faked it a
little."

I thought so myself, but I wouldn't admit it, even
to him.

But the funny part of it is that now when we look at the photograph, there's hardly a shadow of hair on that funny little head. She has jolly eyes, and her bona fide grin, all right. But to tell you the truth, she's as bald as an egg. Yet somehow, because we loved her so much, we saw hair!

Anyway, I've kept at her hair. A few weeks ago I turned it over to her to brush. It was to be her full responsibility. Then I discovered that her method, though mathematically correct, was far from orthodox. Instead of brushing a hundred strokes a day, she waited until Saturday, did seven hundred at once, and fell prostrate.

"I better *had* be beautiful," she said threateningly. "All this valuable time I'm wasting on it."

Then I remembered something that happened yesterday, and I wrote that down for Peter and had to open the envelop again to put it in with the other pictures.

"Darling, I had a talk with your child about beauty yesterday," I said to him. "You know the way those talks go ... good practical stuff, and then a little eight-year-old philosophy about it.

" 'Your father and I want you to grow up and be a beautiful person,' I said to her. 'As beautiful as Sylvia Cedric.'

" 'I don't want to be beautiful like Sylvia,' Boo said.

" 'You don't?'

" 'I want to grow up and be beautiful like Lilliam.' "

I put that little snapshot in with the others; it seemed to me a portrait of his daughter a man would like to have, there among the sand and dirt and ugliness.

VI

Straight vs. Curly

Long ago we all got used to having Janet be the smart one. We know now before any of our children meet in contest that it will be Janet who wins. We're so reconciled to it that we don't even hold it against Janet. In fact, what we're excited about is second place.

Janet could read before any other child in school. She could add before anybody else had the faintest idea what counting meant, except that it was some kind of nursery rhyme that didn't make any sense. Now that they've all got over the first droll hurdles of learning, Janet is still out ahead, finishing every paper the first one in the class, and never so much as an eye dotted incorrectly.

I know Janet's mother never has any of the scenes that we have over learning, those clashes between the unmarshaled forces of ignorance and the neat phalanxes of symbols which we have agreed shall spell a word.

"But there are so many ways you could spell it," Boo says quite reasonably. "Why couldn't this be my way?"

I remember one day we had to write a composition at home. She sat and sat for an hour, staring happily at a blank page.

"I can't think of anything to say," she said. "At

least not anything small enough," she added cheerfully.

I went away and left her; I came back casually to see how it was going, and still the blank page and she stared at each other.

"I don't know how to start."

"At the beginning, dear," I said gently.

"There isn't any beginning," she said. "I'm supposed to write about the lovely fish farm. But it doesn't begin anywhere. *I've* been going on and on ever since I was born."

I saw what she meant. Whatever happens to you joins itself to that already-flowing stream of your consciousness, and how can you know where to snip it off and say, "This is the beginning"? There is no beginning. . . .

But I pretended I didn't understand what she meant, so that I could make the thing seem reasonable. I explained about chapters, and she looked intelligent, and I left her, hopefully.

But only idleness emanated from her room, and at last she came to my door.

"I don't know how to begin it, but I do know how it ends," she said. "Can I begin with the end?"

That sounded reasonable; I've seen lots of things I knew how to end, with no idea how to begin them. So I agreed that was all right, and she skipped back to her room. But only more quietness issued forth. At last I went in to see.

To my amazement, the page was still blank.

"Well, I've started it, anyway," she said.

"Where?" I asked grimly.

"I've put down the last thing." She looked up at me

utterly serious and unmischievous. Sure enough, down in the right-hand corner, was a period.

I must say Janet bears her superiority rather gracefully, for some one only eight.

"Sometimes she makes out like she doesn't know things," Emmett McDermott says, according to Boo. "I guess she wants people to like her better."

I guess maybe she does, and probably she has discovered that superiority and popularity are by no means synonyms, humans being what we are . . . at any age.

But the children, I suspect, forgive her more easily than do we parents. We pretend to each other that it's all a joke, but I have an idea we all wish Janet's family would move away and give us a chance.

I thought surely that chance had come when I found Janet was going to the day camp this summer.

"This will balance things up," I said to myself. "Janet'll probably be all thumbs on the games and sports. Top-heavy, that's what she is." I pictured our own nimble child outstripping her, for Boo turns somersaults and does hand stands as a kind of doodling on the blank page of the air.

But no. Janet won the races. Janet could float in the swimming class before the other children had got their chests wet. And in the riding circle, before the others could even mount properly, Janet could post like an air mail stamp.

Frankly, I get a little fed up with Janet. But Boo is entirely philosophic about her.

"Janet's just smart," she says cheerfully. "I think maybe it's because she's got nice straight hair."

I might have thought she meant that smartness somehow compensated for straight hair, except that I know Boo admires straight hair.

"What's hair got to do with it?"

"Well, you know. It's straight and nice. It makes up its mind where it's going, and then it gets there without changing it in another direction." She tried her best to explain, and finally I realized that she had a feeling that Janet's hair is just a matter of general efficiency, like the rest of her. The shortest distance between two points. No loitering nor exploring. Just getting there . . . *straight*.

But one day Miss Boo came home from day camp looking unusually pleased with herself.

"We had a treasure hunt," she said.

"That's nice, darling," I said absently, not even asking who had won, because I knew.

"They passed out slips of paper," Boo explained, "and the papers had flowers' names written on them. We went out by ourselves and we were supposed to bring in all the flowers written on the paper. And the one who brought in the most . . ."

"I see, dear. Well, that was very nice, wasn't it?"

She looked at me, gave a kind of hop out of sheer triumphant good spirits, and said, "Guess who won?"

"Why, Janet, I suppose," I said without bitterness.

"Nope," she said in a gulp.

Then she took a bouquet of lollipops out of her pocket and blushingly gave them to me. "This was the prize," she said. "I brought it home to you. But don't let's eat 'em. Let's keep 'em forever. Or maybe give them to my children later. And tell them about how I won them."

"Why ... darling ..." I blushed myself, I was so pleased. Maybe she was going to be a naturalist. ...

Then an unworthy explanation occurred to me.

"I suppose Janet wasn't there to-day," I said grimly.

"Oh yes," she said, looking a shade smug, "Janet was there. She did very well, Miss Grover said. Very well indeed." She gave another hop, and I felt like doing one also. "But I won."

Sure enough, she took from another pocket a bedraggled handful of flowers. When I looked at them, I saw not flowers, but their difficult names written on a slip of paper in Miss Grover's printing. Gypsophila, zinnia, snapdragon, spiderwort, nasturtium.

"But Boo ... were these names written on the paper?"

"Yep," she said nonchalantly. "Most of 'em, I guess. Maybe I have a few extra for good measure."

"But darling ... those are quite big words ... how did you manage to read them?"

She looked up at me with azure innocence in her eyes.

"Oh, I couldn't read *any* of the words," she said wistfully. "So I just went out in the garden, and I picked one of everything I saw. Miss Grover said I did wonderfully."

And that, probably, is the curly-haired way of getting there.

VII

Word from Annabelle

WE had all forgotten about Annabelle, because so many things had happened to us.

There is a strange unreal quality about life, when the important things all seem to happen to you by mail. During the days, and sometimes the weeks, when no letter comes from Peter, I make myself play the grim games which must be familiar to you, too. I pretend I'm not expecting a letter; I watch the clock to see how long I can let the mail lie in the box at the end of our drive, and then I watch to see if I can walk-not-run to get it.

When days go by, the thought of the letter lies like an ache under everything I do or think. Over and over I go through the suspense, the silly self-torture. But never with the top of my mind. That behaves itself. That keeps cheerful and busy; that gets tired out with work, but so thin that the blackness beneath shines through like a bruise.

There are many devices we have all learned for getting through these days when there is no place to let the heart lie down happily and rest. But the best device of all is to live so exhaustingly in the moment that there is nothing left.

"Suppose the letter does come," I reason with myself.

"He never writes anything anyway. He's such a stingy man with his words ... writes like somebody leaning on a telegraph office counter ... *oh, but God please let one come. ..."*

With so much else to think of, we had forgotten Annabelle. Whenever Tom and Lisa came to our house, in the brief times between Lisa's engagements, nobody mentioned Annabelle at all. Lisa usually did most of the talking, because she was brimful of her work.

"I take everything that comes," she said. "Even radio parts, because they may lead to something good. Turner says he'll surely get me a summer-theater job. Ogunquit, probably."

Tom looked glum, and when Lisa noticed it, she said, "Oh, don't worry about him. He's going up with me, and we'll take a darling little cottage, and he'll write that book he used to talk about."

Tom still didn't look too enthusiastic about it; he pulled on his pipe and said, "Oh, sure ... be something to keep me out of the way."

Boo brightened up. "Maybe you could take care of—" she started to say, but I glared at her so menacingly that she dwindled into decent silence.

But before the summer had started, before Tom's classes at Harvard were over, we had a postcard from him. It was addressed to Boo herself, and I recognized Tom's thorny handwriting even though his signature wasn't on the card.

The message said, *"Dear Miss Boo: Please come and see me when I am one day old, sometime in the winter."*

It was signed *"Annabelle."*

VIII

That Cukey

"THAT Cukey," Lilliam says, "he see right through you. Cain't keep no secrets from Cukey. Not in this house."

She laughs to herself, scolding him and boasting about him at the same time as she goes about her canning—Lilliam's eternal canning, which is going to keep us so busy eating this winter that we'll have time for nothing else.

"Know what he tole me this mawnin'?"

"I couldn't possibly guess."

She looks at him triumphantly, as if she expected he was going to leap out of his high chair and try to stop her.

"Now you hesh, Cukey," she says warningly, but Cukey sits morosely silent, utterly indifferent.

"He say, 'Momma, what for don' Missy take her breakfast in bed lak she allus used to?'"

"Hmn," I think to myself. "What has become of my breakfast in bed, anyway?"

"I say, 'Cukey, you hesh yo' mouf. Don' be talkin' to me 'bout what Missy do and don't do.' But Cukey jes laff fit to kill. 'Missy come down here to see *me* bright an' early.'" Lilliam looks utterly scandalized at what she is reporting. You can see she is prepared to

go right over and spank that Cukey for his conceited-
ness if I say so. But my face must reassure her, for she
goes on: "Cukey say, 'Missy come down here to see how
is I gittin' along. Missy can't hardly wait to see if I is
likin' my breakfast.'"

I look at Cukey, and he grins shamelessly. For once,
his face fits his dialogue, for he looks both bold and
embarrassed.

I don't have my breakfast in bed any more. My only
luxury, my sole, cherished indulgence, my one vanity
and spoiling . . . has vanished from my life. And I had
not even realized it had gone until Cukey explained it
braggingly, as a compliment to himself.

"I guess he's right," I admit, and I prod him in his
ginger-bread ribs—at least in the general location where
he ought to have ribs—and I say: "Just you wait, Cukey,
my lad. Yesterday I ordered you a little white coat. The
middle of next week, I expect you to bring up my
breakfast tray at seven o'clock."

Lilliam is delighted. "That'll fix him," she says in a
whisper, and she looks at him with adoring malice.
"You do it, Missy. Sits round here doin' nuffin. Givin'
everybody orders and doin' nuffin hisse'f. Time he got
usefuller around here."

But Cukey knows how useful he is. He looks to me
like somebody who appreciates his value in good round
numbers, and then hangs on a couple of zeros, just to
make the sum more whoppin'.

Boo, who has heard this conversation, is mildly dis-
turbed about it. "Are you really?" she says, as soon as
we are out of the kitchen again. "The middle of next
week? Are you really?"

"A little white coat," I say firmly.

Her loyalty flames up in her face. "He's already terribly useful around the house," she says.

"In what way?" I ask as fiercely as possible.

"Well, he's somebody you can kind of sit and look at. And maybe tell secrets to. He's not exactly our baby, but we can have him all we want to, to hug and everything."

He is, in fact, a handy little receptacle to catch the rich overflow of love from too-full hearts. He takes anything you give him and makes no complaints. At this stage he's part animal and part vegetable and all pet. Something not so frisky and destructive as a goat, and more interesting than an ornamental shrub, sitting on the grass beside the drive. Lilliam keeps him staked out at the end of a sparkling white clothes-line, and she goes out and moves him every hour or so, following the sun around his stake.

"Doctor say, 'Give him plenty sunshine,'" Lilliam says. "I say, 'Mr. Doctor, that Cukey ain't gwine get no more sun-tan than he is.'"

The only thing Lilliam rebels at in the doctor's program is cod-liver oil.

"Castor oil, but no cod-livers," she says firmly.

"But Lilliam, why not?"

"Doctor say that keep him from being nice and bow-legged."

"But . . ."

"It on-natural for a chile not to be bow-legged when he first gits up an' walks. Gives him a kind of bounce to his walk. Cukey gwine be nice and bow-legged." She looks at me with woman-to-woman hostility, warning me not to try to interfere.

"Besides," she says, "Joseph likes bow-legged babies. Bow-legged babies are good luck. Chicken got a wishbone for good luck, and baby got bow-legs."

IX

First Fear

W<small>HEN</small> we met the word fear in a fairy story, I used to have to explain what it was.

"Well, you see, the children didn't trust the witch. 'Fear' means not to trust," I would explain, hoping I was planting no dangerous seeds in the sub-soil of her mind.

Then something came into our simple world which meant that never again would I have to define fear. Miss Boo knew what it meant. Where before neither height nor depth nor any other creature had ever threatened, now there was something terrifying that darkened the sky, the very sky over our heads.

The first time I saw him I was in a car. He was sitting meekly beside the drive of the new people who had moved in up the road from our house.

"Umn," I thought a bit self-centeredly. "That'll be nice. Miss Boo'll have him to play with. Just what she needs."

Before I'd had time to tell her about him, Lilliam came screaming into the back door, with her apron on backward, where he had clutched at it and tried to hold her.

"He's ten foot tall. . . . He chewed the back outen my dress. . . . He was fixin' to chew off my arm, but I ran...." She had an empty plate in her hand, where some of her biscuits had been a few minutes before. She slumped into her kitchen chair and fanned herself with the plate.

She had been walking up the road with the biscuits, swaddled in a napkin, in one hand, and a jar of strawberry preserves in the other, and this hurricane with flapping jaws and paws had come charging out at her. He breathed fire; he had forty teeth in his jaws; he put his great-big-heavy paws on her shoulders and reached up to where she was trying to hold the biscuits out of his reach, and ate them in one gulp. He laughed all over his face, and then he tried to chew up her apron....

"He was probably only trying to be friendly," I said uncertainly. But I didn't convince even myself.

I went up the road in the afternoon to see. He heard me coming, and he was there to meet me, a charging Goliath, and me with no slingshot and a congenital suspicion of dogs.

"Nice doggie, nice doggie," I said vaguely, and sure enough he took it as encouragement and leaped up to look closely into my face. He was, it seemed to me, the biggest dog I had ever seen. His ears flapped and his red-rimmed eyes glowed and his teeth were an inch long.

The new people came out and called to me.

"Don't be afraid of him," they said hospitably. "He's only a puppy."

In my terror, I thought, "If he's a puppy, he's going to be a dinosaur when he gets his growth."

The man, a nice pleasant chap, ran down to meet me

and spoke sharply to the beast, who put his forepaws reluctantly back on the earth.

"Heavens, he's big, isn't he?" I said breathlessly.

"I see you like dogs," the new neighbor said. "He's a fine boy. A little too friendly at the moment. But he'll get over all that exuberance with a little training."

He kept his hand on the puppy's collar, but even so, I felt uncomfortable. We talked about our town, and he told me nice things about his family, and I tried to say how glad we were that they had moved in.

"I have a little girl," I said.

"That's great. She's going to like Pointsettia."

"Oh . . . you have a little girl, too?"

He laughed robustly. "No. This big sissy here. You see, his mother was a setter and his father was a pointer. The name was inevitable, wasn't it?" You could see how much he liked the whole thing. So I tried to.

"You let your little girl come up and play with him all she wants to," he said. "Pointsettia likes children."

I felt like saying, "With salt and pepper, I imagine," but that seemed unneighborly, so I just smiled as best I could, and went home.

I tried to prepare Boo.

"You know what we've always said this neighborhood needed?" I said valiantly.

"A nice swimming-pool?"

"No, darling. A nice dog."

I saw from her face that Lilliam had told her.

"A nice *little* dog," she said.

I thought fast, trying to hide my utter agreement with her amendment. "Funny thing about dogs," I said. "They never have the faintest idea what size they are."

"Haven't they?"

"We used to have an Old English Sheepdog, you know. I've told you about Mopsie. Well, Mopsie honestly believed he was a lap-dog, and if he didn't feel well, or if we had been away for a few days, he'd try to sit in my lap. He was as big as a laprobe and hung down all around me, but he really believed he fitted fine."

"Is this dog like a laprobe?" she said disspiritedly.

"No . . . he's more like . . ." I tried to think of some simile that would present him in a winsome light, and rejected "fire-engine" and "tank" and "elephant herd" quickly. "Well, he's *friendly*," I said firmly. "He jumps up on you to show how friendly he is."

I hadn't noticed that Lilliam had come to the door.

"Ain't gwine show *me* how friendly he is," she said with the first belligerence I had ever heard in her gentle voice.

"Lilliam says she'll fix him," Boo said timidly.

"What'll you do to fix him?" I asked, hoping she had some good old magic method brought up from the South of her childhood.

She looked me in the eye with hostile determination, as if the dog had been my idea. "Efn that dog has moved in," she said coldly, "I'se gwine move right outen here."

Boo looked at her desperately, and I could see that in her mind she had galloped up the steps and had thrown a few things into her little bag, abandoning our house and home to go wherever Lilliam went. I ran up behind them, in my mind, and packed my own bag.

We all stood in bleak silence a terrible moment, realizing the extent of the trouble that had suddenly come upon us.

"Nonsense," I said sternly to all of us, sensibly unpacking my bag and coming back downstairs to dignity and adulthood. "Nonsense," I said again, but I was frightened. This had been such a nice place yesterday ... and now we were in double danger. We had gained an unwelcome dog, and we might lose our Lilliam.

X

Stories

NOTHING's real until it's in a story. If something happens to you, it may or may not have been just your imagination, but if somebody tells it to you in a story, then there are two of you who know it, and you can support each other against any dissenters.

A day may have as many faces as there are people who live it, but a story is something concrete and solid that you can get the teeth of your credulity into. A day may be all in the way you look at it, but a story is fixed forever, like good paint on a canvas.

The first few years of their lives, fiction and fact are almost interchangeable. If you tire of one you touch it up with the other, and both are improved. They are two worlds, each transparent, so that the other can shine through.

"I know it isn't true," Miss Boo says sometimes, now that she is "big," "but I like to believe it anyway."

I know that is "bigger" even than it sounds, for it is the pattern of many of our most mature illusions. Only adults don't admit it so honestly. It certainly is the basis of many love affairs.... The trick, of course, the sublime and perilous trick, is to go on believing what we know isn't true.

At Miss Boo's size one doesn't get into too much trouble by skipping back and forth across the hopscotch line drawn between stories and actual fact. Sometimes she leaves you standing on one foot, on the wrong side of the line, while she hops blithely off in the other territory and wins the game.

"Pooh, anybody knows that's only make-believe," she says with scornful disloyalty, after you've contributed some detail to the picture you were both taking seriously.

You know that must happen; it means she is growing up. She must accept, one syllable at a time, what we have all agreed are the facts of life.

"That's right," you say meekly. "It *is* only make-believe, isn't it?"

Time was, you remember—only a year ago—when make-believe was completely reputable. Its territory was unassailable, and the people who tried to dispel it just didn't *know*.

There was a day, not so very long ago, when I heard her upstairs carrying on a dialogue with herself. One side was nagging and strident; the answers were soft and apologetic.

I went up, and she was sitting alone in the center of her bed, looking not too happy.

"What seems to be the matter?" I said sympathetically.

"We're query-ling," she said.

"Oh, I'm sorry."

"My make-believe friend doesn't like me," Boo said in shame. "She doesn't like anything I do."

"Well..." I tried to think of some way of making

Boo more acceptable to her friend. "Have you been nice to her?"

"I've tried to be," she said earnestly. "I give her everything she wants. But she just doesn't like me."

Then I did an unforgivable thing. I said spitefully, "Well, I'd fix *her*."

"What would you do?"

"I wouldn't *make-believe* her any more."

Boo looked at me in horror.

"Oh, I couldn't do that," she said. "That would make her mother feel so badly."

"All right. Then I wouldn't *make-believe* her mother either." She looked at me then as if I were not only a murderer but a double-murderer.

"Oh, no," she said in such a whisper that I was utterly ashamed of myself.

"I'll tell you what," I said brightly after a moment. "You girls both come downstairs and have some cookies, and I'll let you both try on my new hat."

"Will you?" Boo said delightedly. Then she glanced inquiringly at her make-believe friend, and thank heaven her friend was pleased, too.

But that period of whole-hearted make-believe has passed, and we're supposed to be glad to see it going. The transition is the shadowy land we're in now, and that too we'll pass through sometime, into the world which adults have subdued into humdrumness.

Except when we tell about it to others. Then it rouses itself into a sparkle. Most of the best things that happen to us happen in stories. Telling about it afterward is the glittering frosting on much soggy cake. Indeed, some of us would scarcely bother with the cake except as something to hold the frosting.

Part of education, of course, is to make fact as acceptable as fiction. They begin working on it early nowadays in school. Needless to say, the story-telling is Miss Boo's favorite subject.

"We stand up in the front of the room and tell things," she says, and she is breathless at the mere memory of such delight. She isn't a bit sensitive about the fact that Miss Bailey leaves her until the very end of the class and then has to suggest that she break the story in half and finish it to-morrow.

"There's never time to tell all of mine," she says regretfully. One thing leads to another with Miss Boo; there isn't a crack in her infinity as wide as a spider's whisker.

The stories that I like to hear about are the ones told by Emmett McDermott. I've never seen Emmett McDermott, but I know him well, having listened to him thousands of times at dinner-parties, on golf courses, in trains, and even, I regret to say, in my own voice. The world is full of him, and he always has tireless lungs.

This particular Emmett, like the rest of them, is a solid citizen. Although he is only seven now, he is already bald in effect, and he has an incipient paunch. He's cheerful to a fault, and he's never seen, nor ever will see, anything that is past explaining. He was born with his feet on the ground.

Miss Bailey knows she can count on Emmett when she asks who wants to tell a story. Emmett McDermott always puts up his hand, and I have no doubt that something spurts up in Miss Bailey's heart and she says to herself, "Maybe *this* time . . ."

So she says, brightly, "All right, Emmett. You tell us some lovely adventure you had yesterday."

Emmett gets up, metaphorically lays down his black cigar, and clears his throat. He looks around with a grim glint in his eye, the glint of a nail that is going to be hammered solidly into anything that tries to escape, be it fact or listener.

He takes a big breath. "Came home," he says. "Changed my coat, got my baseball, went out, played a while, came in, ate dinner, took a bath, went to bed."

Miss Boo relates all this to me in Emmett's voice. A cheerful, determined singsong, which I recognize wearily well.

"He certainly does enjoy his stories," she says placidly, with no mischief in her face. But the precocious mischief in her body makes a frisky little spring of it. She goes on with Emmett McDermott's voice sawing away through the planks of his tale.

"Got up, ate a griddle cake, brushed my teeth," she continues. She is on the floor now, preparing to flip into a somersault. "Put on my coat, came to school."

She gets up after the somersault, and her body seems to feel a little better, released from the restriction of Emmett's mind. She doubles over and looks upside down at me, through the ruffled inverted V of her panties.

Her face is deadly serious as she says, "I certainly wouldn't want to marry Emmett McDermott, would you? Well, only for a little while, maybe."

She lets her forehead touch the ground lightly and rolls over in a silent somersault. It is the perfect punctuation for all the Emmetts' stories. A ho-hum of the whole body.

XI

A Stickler for Form

JUST when I think I'll never get our Miss Boo civilized . . . never inculcate the idea that there is a proper way to do everything, and a proper tool for doing it . . . something like this happens.

Until Peter left, Miss Boo had had about four letters in her whole life—not counting the advertisements, which she knows don't have her name on them but which belong to her by common consent.

One day, the fifth letter arrived, and it was from her father. It had her name written in his great sprawling handwriting, and when I saw it in my mail, I felt as if I had been telescoped out of my own life into some distant day. Your baby's name on an envelop . . . suddenly private and separate from you . . . is always a shock. But when it is written in that one handwriting which can stop your heart after nearly ten years . . .

"Any mail for me?" she said with routine hopefulness when I brought in the collection.

"Yes. With your name on it." I tried to disguise my excitement so she could enjoy every atom of the experience.

She seized the envelop as if she could scarcely believe it was really hers. She spelled out the letters lingeringly.

I kept myself from snatching it and tearing it open

to see what Peter had written. I offered patiently to read the letter for her.

"No, thank you," she said. "If I need your help later . . ."

She took it and flew upstairs to her room, breathless with suspense. I felt as if a strange woman had suddenly stepped between me and Peter. I wanted to run upstairs behind her. But after all, this was one-fifth of her lifetime's correspondence, and she had her rights.

I could hear her dashing around her room, mumbling to herself in a frenzy of excitement. I waited downstairs, hardly breathing in my impatience. Suppose she didn't invite me to read it at all! But knowing Peter's handwriting, and Boo's inability to read anything but print at this point, I felt pretty sure that couldn't happen.

But she didn't come back.

I waited and waited, until my frenzy was surging. I called upstairs, edgily well-controlled.

"Don't you want me to help you read your letter, dear?"

"Yes," she said, "but wait, please."

More suspense; five minutes of scurrying around the room frantically, as if she were a squirrel trying to find the right place to bury a nut. I could hear her muttering . . . almost sobbing with her own maddening slowness.

At last she came running down the steps, pale with excitement.

"I thought I'd never find my letter opener," she said.

XII

A Date with Annabelle

Wᴇ didn't wait, of course, to go and pay our respects to Annabelle. We went straight over to the Kings' apartment in Cambridge, and we looked like Christmas, because we had all sorts of presents we *had* to take.

"She's got to have my first baby blanket," Boo said. "And she'll want a tea set. . . ."

"But, dear, she's not born yet. They don't play with tea sets until much, much later."

"I could send Button Eyes," she said. "He's had a lot of experience."

But the fact was, Button Eyes couldn't be spared. He is still, after seven years, the best of the lot to sleep with. He is furry, but bald in spots, and squashy; all his lumps know how to arrange themselves when you hug him, and if he falls out of bed, he just grins up at you and says nothing.

All the way in to Boston on the train and out to Cambridge on the subway, Miss Boo talked.

"They'll make good payrents," she said. "They look like fathersnmothers."

"How do fathersnmothers look?"

It was a word hard to define. She thought about it a long while, and after I had practically forgotten what we were talking about, she said earnestly, "Well, a baby would know. A baby would recognize them anywhere."

"Evidently," I agreed. "A baby has, it seems."

"They like each other," she said, screwing up her face in deep thought. "A baby likes to be where people like each other."

Yes, that is true, I thought. Sometimes when you look at two persons . . . not even related to each other except by marriage . . . and realize that they are to be transformed into parents, you see that a miracle is required. Love is the only climate in which such miracles are indigenous. So babies ought to pick parents terribly in love. If hearts are full already, there is always room in them for a child. A child *can* fill an empty or a shriveled heart, but it isn't happy work, and it doesn't make the kind of human being the world most needs.

"Uncle Tom means things when he says 'em," Boo was saying. "When he wants to go home, he says, 'C'mon, Lisa, time to go home!' "

I knew what she meant. Tom lets Lisa frolic about on a long rope, but when he so much as twitches it, she comes.

A father should know how to say "No," and mean it; and "Yes," and stand behind it. That represents security to a child; a child needs to count on that as grown-ups need to count on God.

"And of course Aunt Lisa makes-believe," Boo said.

That required no explaining, for we both understood that well. A mother who can't make-believe . . . who can't transform crackers-as-usual into a picnic, or a bedspread into a tent, or nothing at all into a whole new world . . . just hasn't any right inviting children.

Miss Boo was going on. "They like to talk. Uncle Tom's always asking questions. 'How come?' he says."

I saw what she meant; it's what I like best about Tom myself. A child can't help liking to be with people who have popcorn under their skulls ... any more than the rest of us can help liking it.

"Yes," I said, as we were walking up the stairs to Lisa's apartment, which is on the second floor of an old mansion and which always looks as if it were expecting Oliver Wendell Holmes, "I think Annabelle's making no mistake. There are a few little changes that will have to be made, I suppose. But, after all, the only person who can make parents out of people is a baby."

Inside the big living-room with the bleached mahogany bookshelves towering ceiling high, and the matching drum tables completing the matching fireplace chairs, we could already see signs of Annabelle's approach.

The amusingly formal room was "expecting" all right ... but not Oliver Wendell. Lisa had moved her row of dramaturgical books to a shelf high out of her own reach and had replaced them with a tomey row of handbooks on baby care.

"Tom used to keep these in a box under his bed," she said when I mentioned them. "He was very sheepish about them. Been collecting them since before he went to college. I think maybe I was ... jealous."

Boo was already looking at the pictures.

"This isn't the way you pin a diaper," she said, expertly. Lisa looked at the illustration quizzically.

"Oh no," she said. "They wear 'em like sarongs now."

"Only more concentrated," I suggested.

Lisa was reaching for a cigarette; then she remembered something her doctor must have said, for she closed the pewter box again firmly.

"We've signed a new lease for this apartment, to run another year," she said. "It has a wonderful garden for the baby pen. That's why Tom rented it in the first place, nearly a year ago."

Then she saw there was something a bit wistful in that sentence, so she added jauntily, "Tom says that when things get too crowded, *he'll* go out and sit in the baby pen."

"They aren't any trouble," Boo said in a rush of defense. "You hardly know they're in the house." You'd have thought she had brought up three or four generations of them. "Most of the time," she added honestly.

Lisa looked at her a long moment. And then a flush crept up her long lovely throat, and a smile began in the depths of her eyes and finally touched her lips.

"I want to know they're in the house, Boo," she said. "I want to know that more than anything else on earth."

The moment was dissolving in discomfort, for neither Lisa nor Boo was used to so much emotion.

"You'll know it," I said a bit grimly, "and don't let anybody tell you you won't." Then we looked at each other and we both laughed.

"I just hope I'm not going to be a flop," Lisa said. "This is one play that can't close if the plot's no good. I just hope I've got *brains* enough to be good at it."

She wasn't somebody condescending reluctantly to giving in to nature. She was a woman who had worked up into a higher job, and she knew it. I had never liked Lisa so much as at that moment.

"You'll be good enough," I said confidently. "Don't you worry about it, Lisa. I know you had lots of wonderful plans, but . . ."

She looked at me in honest bewilderment.

"Plans?" she said. "What plans?"

I saw that Annabelle already had the situation well in hand.

XIII

Imagination Is So Nice

ONCE a week Miss Boo goes to a dancing class at our country club. We send her so she won't stumble over her shoestrings or dislocate her own wrist; we send her so she'll get accustomed to herself in acceptable motion.

Not that she doesn't know how to dance better than they'll ever teach her. She's had to unlearn some of her grace; she's had to learn how to curtsy and to smirk instead of to swarm at you, with her welcome wagging all over like a puppy's. But she might as well learn decorum young. She knows how to excuse herself politely when she must leave the room, tiptoeing creakily, as if she had a tack in her heel. She's learned how to apologize.

("But for *what?*" she kept asking logically when Miss Sprockett was teaching them. Plainly the whole class wanted to do something wrong, first. Might as well get something out of the apology, you could see they were thinking.)

Besides all these formal usages, Miss Sprockett has also dipped lustily into the fountain of imagination. When she persuaded us to let Boo join the class, she went into that quite thoroughly, looking a little perspiry in her earnestness.

"Yes, indeed, I quite agree," I kept saying, trying to spare her the discomfort of explaining the joys of imagination to me. It's been my shy observation that the people who are willing to talk about imagination seldom have much. Imagination is a guilty secret, usually, a possession best kept inside the privacy of one's own skull.

But I'm always eager to coöperate with Miss Boo's education. Miss Sprockett's children are well-mannered and subdued, and if developing imagination produces that, we decided we'd give it a whirl.

The dancing class doesn't approach it light-heartedly; imagination is a systematic business. You decide what you imagine, and then you do it. It doesn't pop into the head. In spite of Miss Sprockett's figure of speech when she mentions it to parents, imagination is not so much a fountain as a slab of marble, to be chiseled and hacked at.

But the children enjoy it. One day they pretend they're this, and the next lesson they pretend they're that, and usually Miss Boo limps along behind them, awkwardly graceful and grimly spontaneous.

Miss Sprockett says, "To-day we're going to be autumn leaves. We're hanging on the limb of a tree; we flutter back and forth; we play with the wind, but the tree holds us fast. The wind tugs at us, but the tree holds us fast."

Miss Sprockett, her eyes half-closed, her voice melodious, goes on: "Now some of us tear loose ... we flutter to the ground, we swirl, we dance ... we are free ... all of us are free now.... Come, Walter, you're free, dear.... We break into mad dancing now...."

Walter looks about as free as a ship's anchor, but he is trying terribly hard. His mother, sitting next to me, knitting furiously and pretending not to pay too much attention, is grimacing at him encouragingly.

You get the idea. Sometimes they're bunny rabbits; sometimes they're goldfish, or a kite in a March wind, or a flower on its stalk, or a deer, or practically anything.

I have no doubt it does them all good. "People," so Miss Sprockett tells me when we talk self-consciously about it after the lesson, while I wait for Miss Boo to get one last drink at the country-club water-cooler, "ought to get *out* of themselves more."

"Indeed they ought to," I say enthusiastically, wondering when we'll get *out* of this afternoon.

At last we're alone, on our way home, walking now because we mustn't use the car for pleasure such as this.

"You had a lovely time," I say enthusiastically, in case there's any doubt about it.

But there is no doubt. She dances all the way home, running ahead of me, and prancing. When we get home she is still full of it. A half-hour after we've come into the house I hear her up in her room, dancing and dancing.

I go up after a while, casually, to see. She smiles at me over her shoulder; she is swooping and stooping, and then yearning upward, working out some pattern of her own. I try to know intuitively what she is being. A young tree growing? A snowstorm? A cloud across the sky?

"What are you now?" I ask.

"Now," she says, stopping to look at me with almost hostile matter-of-factness:

"Now, I'm a little girl dancing in her bedroom."

Then we smile at each other, quite understanding.

XIV

Lilliam's Stars

Thursday in our house used to be Lilliam's day off. But now there are no more of those trips into the mysterious city, which she used to tell us about on Friday. That wonderful world of Lilliam's, made up of strangers in their best clothes, who smiled at her and always told her very politely where the chicken barbecue place was and then went along with her to show her, when they discovered from her voice that she was up from the country...those congenial strangers who finally partook of the chicken with her and invited her home to meet their children and their husbands, and ended up, likely as not, by coming from jes up the branch from where Cousin Marty-Blake was born...that world of Lilliam's has been put away now, as all our worlds have.

But war for Lilliam is nothing in head-lines, nothing concerned with maps or munitions or treaties. War for Lilliam is something you read about in the Bible.

"World jes got so swole up with badness, people who fixin' to do right has got to march off and fight," Lilliam says.

The war will end when all of us stop hating and quarreling and getting the best of each other. We'll know it's over when we feel our ownse'fs thinking first of the will of God and last of the will of almighty us. It's as simple as that.

If you asked Lilliam where *is* the war, she'd say, "Why, right wherever is two people ain't lovin' each other like themse'fs."

War came into our house by the front door and by the back. It came in an official envelop and took Joseph. Joseph went down and told the man that he was going to be a Daddy, and the man said, "Sorry, son, but that'll jes make you a better soldier."

"Joseph has been chose," Lilliam says when she tells any one about it. She makes it sound as if it were God Himself who had leaned out of His cloud, put on His gold-rimmed glasses to scrutinize the race, and then laid His gentle finger on Joseph.

Soon after Joseph left, Lilliam went into Boston, dressed in her Thursday clothes.

"I wanna git us-all two stars, like people hang in windows," she said.

But she came home without a service flag. "Ain't good enough," she said. "Gotta look some place higher up next Thursday. This gotta be good, sure enough. Quality, this gotta be."

But the next Thursday she came home again without a flag.

"Nuffin' but trash-flags," she said scornfully. "I'se gwine make this flag my ownse'f."

She had found heavy white satin, and as soon as luncheon was over, she borrowed my ruler and drew a border, to be embroidered solidly with red silk.

"How are you going to draw in the stars?" I asked.

And she said, "I don't rightly know yet. But my mind will tell me."

Her mind did tell her the next week, and when she brought it home, it was a star-shaped cookie cutter, for her to trace around.

She worked on it day after day, sitting like a vestal priestess with a sheet spread over her lap and down on the floor all around her, as if some arrogant dust might spring up from the carpet and attack the wonderful symbol. The antimacassar which had been her love letter to Joseph had been worked in cross-stitch. But this was too important for any quick-growing cross-stitch. This was needlepoint, finer than snow ... atomically fine. It grew not by inches but by hairs' breadths, day after day. Before it was finished, Cukey was almost ready to be born, but no infant clothes displaced it on her lap.

Sometimes, seeing her there, with her dear good head bent, and her silent hands speaking of patience and tenderness, tears came into my eyes, and I thought, "If she wants to hang it in the front door ... if she wants it in the living-room window ... wherever she wants it ... this house will be honored to have it."

I knew there would be persons ... even friends I love ... who would think it "amusing" or "quaint" or some other down-looking word. But it would not matter.

Then Cukey was born, and in the excitement of bringing him home from the hospital, and feeling our whole house recentered to pivot around that droll little dark monarch ("dat piece of sweet devil's-food cake," as Lilliam herself calls him sometimes), I quite forgot the service flag.

It had disappeared completely, and I pictured it wrapped in its sheet, with the skeins of red and blue silk, lying forgotten in the bottom drawer of Lilliam's bureau.

"She's only a child herself," I said, trying to excuse her. "She's got a new rag doll, and you can't blame her for forgetting."

Besides, it had served its purpose, and I knew it was hanging where it did the most good. In Lilliam's heart. And in mine.

But one day I spoke to her about it.

"Now that you've settled down into your old routine again, I suppose you'll have time to go on with your work."

"What work, Missy?"

"Why, the service flag," I said.

She looked at me and smiled. "Why, I finished that long time ago, Missy. Had to sit up couple nights just before Cukey came, so in casen I didn't git back from the hospital."

"You finished it?"

"Didn't I show it to you, Missy? I guess I jes got tangled up with that Cukey 'bout that time."

"But I thought you were going to hang it in our house?" I was surprised at the hurt disappointment in my own voice.

"Lord, honey, I did hang it," she said, beaming all over.

"But where?"

"Why, chile, come up and let me show you," she said happily.

We went up the stairs to the attic. We shoved ourselves around the old picture frames, and the trunks that stay home nowadays, and the chairs with the fallen arches. I tripped over Peter's riding boots, and in a wild absurd mental vision I saw myself carrying one of them downstairs with me to keep in my bedroom. . . .

In one corner of our attic there was a shaft of gold-moted light that came down from a window like the holy pictures in old-fashioned Bibles. Against this sky-light was fastened Lilliam's precious flag, with its two stars looking toward heaven. Standing on a little table just cleared by the dramatic shadow of the flag was a picture of Joseph taken in his lodge regalia, and opposite it a snapshot of Peter, a tall blurred figure on skis.

I thought, for the first time since he had gone, that I was going to weep; I felt that terrible soap-sudsy bubbling of sobs in my throat. So as quickly as I could I stammered, "But . . . nobody can see it up here."

Lilliam looked up at it reverently and touched a corner of Joseph's picture with her apron, as though some dust might have the audacity to intrude upon it.

"No folkses can see it," she said. "But it's no business of any folkses on earth, Missy. I put it where God can see it, efn He looks down at our house."

I didn't try to say anything. I just stood there, and I felt as if God *were* looking down at us, His children, His nearest kinfolks. . . .

"God's got us all on His Mind," Lilliam said softly.

"He's got right smart on His Mind, seems lak. But He can see this, efn He looks down at our house and gets to wonderin' why Joseph ain't cuttin' the grass lak it oughta be cut."

XV

One Letter at a Time

THINGS got no better with Pointsettia. Miss Boo met him alone once on the road.... A half-hour after I had finally quieted her sobbing, I could see her heart still pounding, by the way her pinafore ruffle quivered. Something had to be done about it.

We arranged by telephone; we said we'd like to come up as a family and see Pointsettia.

"Everybody likes him," the Marshalls said confidently just before we hung up. "All you need is to get acquainted with him."

"Yes, I'm sure that's all," I said bravely. "I wish we'd known him when he was first born."

"Well, he's still only a puppy," the Marshalls said, and then, in refutation of the silent thing which was screaming through our minds, "Of course, he's never actually bitten anybody. He only looks as if he intended to."

I tried to explain that to Boo before we paid our call.

"Yes, but..." she kept saying, and then stopped, because there is no logical way to explain fear. The strange and torturing part about fear is that it is always something phrased in the future tense. Fear says, "It never has happened ... but suppose it will happen in a minute!"

Miss Boo was ill after luncheon, at the very thought of going up to visit the lovely new dog in the neighborhood. But I couldn't let her off, for I knew that fear grows in the dark, and I dared not let the darkness stay unfought.

We walked up the road, clutching each other's hands, and Lilliam and Cukey stalked along with us, Cukey balanced on Lilliam's lean hip-bone, which is her way of toting him. Cukey, oblivious and merry, was the only one in the party who was enjoying the walk.

We tried to talk about other things, but we were all thinking of Pointsettia, whose only crime was his size and his terrible friendliness.

"Efn on'y his ears and his jaws didn' flap like they does," Lilliam said. "Efn on'y his teeth wasn't so big."

"It's just silly for us to be afraid of him," I said.

"Yas'm," Lilliam said. "But silly or not silly, I'se jes gwine go on bein'."

The Marshalls took us out in a body to call on him in his nice white doghouse. He clanked his huge chain and grinned at us, and I even fed him a bone.

"Look at that!" I said valiantly. "Doesn't he eat it nicely?"

"He jes chawmp it," Lilliam said. "Efn it was a piece of piecrust he couldn't chawmp it mo' easy."

The bone, in fact, was a mistake, for he ground it to powder horribly before our very eyes, and we were all thinking the same thing, and it was hideous. It gave our fear a definite screen upon which to project its pictures.

"That was a cow's joint, that bone . . . and he ate it like a pretzel. A little girl's wrist . . ." I said all that without words in the silence and privacy of my own terror, and when I glanced at Boo, I saw she had put her hands behind her.

When we finally got home again I said, "Now see! There wasn't a thing to be afraid of, was there?"

And Lilliam said nothing, and Boo didn't appear to hear me. Only Cukey looked at me and grinned.

Cukey said, in his own way, "Big dawg like that don' like dark meat anyway, mos' likely."

But in the night there was a terrible scream, and I woke up running down the hall to Boo's room, and she was sitting up in bed whimpering and fighting off something. But of course nothing was there, except her terror.

"What was it, darling?"

"It was just something," she said, ashamed to tell me. "It was something that kind of jumped on me when I was asleep. It tried to lick my face. . . ."

Lilliam, wrapped in Joseph's plaid bathrobe, had come close on my heels.

"I had me a nightmare too," she said indignantly. "My mind tell me we ought to move us out of this here place."

At that moment I made up *my* mind that we would move. We'd give up this house we had built according to our needs and the promise of new needs. What did a house matter, actually? We'd find another one. . . .

But in the morning, that seemed extreme and drastic. In the morning there was Peter's big wine-colored leather chair before the library fireplace, and the dimple his head made in the back . . . and there was our garden we had planted together, all the lost Saturdays

... and there was Boo's forty-foot swing he had shinnied up an oak to fasten to a limb. . . . There must be a simpler way, and we would find that.

Lilliam, too, was seeing things around our house that were dear to her, I have no doubt, because of Joseph. It may have been our woodpile, or Joseph's little pine grove, where he once sat on a hot afternoon and ate a whole watermelon "jes lak he dreamt about doin' when he was a little bittie boy."

"Ain't no use that dawg chasin' us outen our house," Lilliam said indignantly in the morning. I could see in her eyes our attic skylight. God had located that skylight with its two stars. God had been taking care of our men. No use mixin' God up by us moving away. . . .

And besides, suppose Joseph didn't get the letter saying just where we'd gone? . . . Suppose he came back after the war was over . . . and nobody knew where we'd gone? . . . I could see all this in Lilliam's casualness.

"No use us lettin' old biggety dawg ruin our home. Besides, don't we-all pay taxes or somethin'?"

"Certainly we do," I said. "And the Marshalls pay all we pay, and dog taxes besides."

"We'll git through the summer. We kin stay home in summertime," Lilliam said. "But what'm we gwine do when fall comes?"

"Fall?"

"Yas'm. How's Miss Boo gwine walk up past that brute eve'y day to the school bus? Ain't gwine be able to. Jes haf give up gwine school, that's what."

She looked at me quickly, and then she said, "Maybe you hafta have little bittie class at home. Cukey and Boo . . . and me."

So ... not being able to read was still her secret shame. Joseph had forgiven it. ... Joseph had laughed at it and had married her anyway. ... But now there was Cukey, and the old shame still held. In his name now.

"Don't you worry about that," I said. "Fall's a long way off. And as for teaching Cukey to read ..."

The room was quiet as it always is when Lilliam has broken down the wall of pride to speak about her sorrow of ignorance.

"I've got a good idea about teaching Cukey to read."

"Yas'm? Who's gwine teach him, Missy?"

"You are, Lilliam."

"I is?"

"You begin with A, and you teach him one letter at a time."

"One letter at a time. Zat all there is to readin'?"

"That's all there is to anything. One letter at a time."

"Um-*hum*," she said wonderingly. "Why, seems lak a person could do jes about anything, one letter at a time. How come nobody evah tole me that?"

XVI

Annabelle by Any Other Name

Lisa and Tom had reached that stage of people acutely in love where they can't resist talking about their beloved to practically anybody who will listen. But casually. And jokingly. Their eyes so shone with this new love that you felt as if you had no right to look.

They came out to our house, and Tom pretended it was only because he wanted to borrow Peter's fancy saw which hangs forlornly in the old workroom.

"I didn't know you were a carpenter," I said.

"I'm not." He grinned, and I could see he was recognizing that this carpentry was just another symptom of what he calls his "prospectiveness." "I'm fixing up a lame woodbox," he said, being very humorous about it. "Lisa picked it up at an auction in Ipswich a long time ago. We kept it beside the fireplace ... remember? But originally it was intended for something else."

"For what?" I said, not remembering the woodbox.

"Why, it was built for a cradle," he said, almost blushing. "One side's kind of weak. Can't have the baby spilling out of it."

Lisa, too, always had a piece of handiwork which made it practically unavoidable that we talk about her favorite subject. Lisa used to be a restless person, whose long legs always seemed twitching to be up and striding about. But now she sits and knits, and if there are babies looking out through the key-hole of heaven, I haven't any doubt they're quarreling about who is going to get her in the raffle. For you never saw a more adorably motherly-looking person in your life. Her hair, which used to be a long drift of silvery-gold about her shoulders, has been pinned up now and is a bouquet of curls on top of her head.

Motherhood is going to be very becoming to Lisa; it gives her color and quietness and mystery. She talks slowly and happily, with a lazy long note in her voice which says there's nothing at all to hurry about. Nothing *can* be hurried, her voice seems to say, soothingly. She moves majestically, rather like a very dignified ship. Tom is a kind of convoy always surrounding her, so proud of her that he has to joke about it. It makes your eyes prickle to see him.

They are at peace with nature, these days. They like Mother Nature very much, and they call her by an affectionate nickname.

"The Old Girl certainly made a sale when she signed up Lisa," Tom says.

Sometimes when he brings in her glass of milk from the kitchen he says, "The Old Girl sent this in."

Lisa said to me, when she finally succumbed to those absurd clothes made for her state, "The Old Girl's designed me one of those comical figures so much in style this year, which billow out in the front."

"Matter of fact, you've never been so good-looking in your life, and you know it," I tell her.

Tom thinks so, too. He can barely keep his eyes off her.

"Look't her," he says boastfully. "You'd think nobody ever had had a baby before. She looks as smug as if she had invented the whole idea." Then he grins ruefully. "Guess maybe I act the same way, don't I?"

"Worse, darling," I tell him.

"Yep. I suppose I do," he says fatuously, with no intention of reforming. "Must make the Old Girl laugh up her sleeve."

They can't decide, of course, whether they expect a boy or a girl. We go into it at length, weighing all the advantages of each; the disadvantages we don't mention—we can't seem to remember what they are. Curiously, we expect both at once, and we speak of The Baby, and then call it interchangeably he and she.

"I've practically decided on the name," Lisa said. "If it's a boy I'm calling him Tomothy."

"You mean Timothy?"

"I mean Tomothy."

"Doesn't that sound a little like a verbal misprint?" I asked gently.

"No. I can't bear Thomas, and he'll be too little to be Tom. I'm calling him Tomothy. I love it."

"And if he's a girl?" I asked, thinking to myself that if he should be a boy, she'll probably call him George, that being the way of parents when they wake up after nine months of blissful irrationality.

"If it's a girl, I'm going to call her Annabelle."

"Annabelle?" I said, as if I'd never heard the name before. "That's nice. For whom, though?"

"It's just a name I thought of," she said guilelessly.

"When I asked Tom how he liked it, he said it was the most remarkable thing."

"Why?"

"Well, it happens to be an old family name."

She smiled at me in all innocence, and I saw she had forgotten that old awkward joke between Tom and Boo, which annoyed her long ago. She had forgotten in the lovely way the Old Girl makes her women forget things.

"Annabelle?" I tried it out again thoughtfully. "I think we'll all like that name."

XVII

Laughter without Apology

A DAY is full of laughter when a child is in the house. A day is a hurdy-gurdy, with unexpected crickety laughter for tunes; it's a penny bank, a house with a child in it, and when you hold it to your ear and shake it, a merry jingle sounds out of it. (Money in a penny bank is never anything urgent: only fun-money destined for ice-cream cones, gum drops, paper dolls, or, at its grimmest, stationery for writing thank-you notes.)

When the world all around is silenced and sober, you stop guiltily sometimes in the midst of your house-laughter and wonder if you've a right to it. Ought *any* of us to laugh, until *all* of us can again, you ask yourself, sometimes. Everybody is supposed to be working and serious, about some job.

And yet, who could be doing a better job than to keep laughter jingling in the pockets of this almost bankrupt world? And who but children could do that job? So let them laugh all they can, and you laugh with them. That's one reason we have 'em.

Sometimes they bring mirth so robust that it has to roll on the floor; sometimes they make you laugh with unspoken amusement that mustn't show on the face, for the sake of some one's small dignity. But you needn't think all the polite laughter which doesn't show on faces is on your side. They laugh at *us;* make no mistake about that. They learn early how impossible it is to explain to us why they find us droll. By the time they are contemporaneous enough to tell us, they too have lost the simple wisdom.

They laugh at our ability to worry, and at our concern for other people's opinions, and at our constant losing of to-day in preparing for to-morrow. Much that we teach them in the name of knowledge is actually organized ignorance, but they learn it with as straight a face as possible, making-believe about it at first, playing it all only as a game. They learn their ignorance slowly, and while they're learning, they practise it in make-believe. But finally the game settles down upon them and becomes the reality, and we both are lost.

Most of their games are sly commentaries on the biggety way we adults live our lives; some are almost allegories as they play them. For instance, Miss Boo is sitting peacefully on the flagstone terrace, singing to herself, frankly bored with the nothing that is happening. She lifts up a leaf absently, and under it there are two lethargic worms slumbering in the shade. She picks up a stick and gives them a prod, hoping each will blame the other. But they are not interested in fighting. She bends over and looks at them closely, and then draws back in alarm, suddenly deciding that it will be fun to be afraid of them.

She leaps up and dashes breathlessly into the kitchen, banging the screen door behind her and turning quickly to lock it.

"What's mattah with you, Miss Boo?" Lilliam says, big-eyed herself.

"Ssh.... Something's chasing me!"

"What kin' of somepin?" Lilliam says, eager to be persuaded to be frightened herself.

"Two worms."

"Worms ... chasin' you-all?" She looks incredulous, her eyes black-and-white apostrophes in her dark face.

"Well, they're getting *ready* to chase me," Boo says.

Lilliam looks at her, and then they burst out laughing together, thoroughly understanding each other.

"Um-hum," Lilliam says. "Sure 'nough. Jes lak ole age fixin' to chase me."

But I, excluded by my grown-upness, know why they laugh so uproariously, both of them. It's the symbolism that tickles them. They can afford to laugh at it, for one of them is too young to be frightened really, and the other too blessed with simplicity. But I can't laugh, for I remember all the times I've been so chased, by catastrophes that didn't happen, by bills and snubs and embarrassments; I remember all the times I have come running in and banged a door shut behind me. Indeed, like most of us in this world, I've run most pantingly to escape ... two worms getting *ready* to chase me.

XVIII

Call for Mrs. Post

WHAT I'd like to know," Boo says, coming home from playing with friends in town. "When *is* it that you get to do what you want?"

"What d'you mean, dear?"

"Well, when I'm the hostess, I have to do what the guests want."

"Yes, that's right."

"And when I'm the guest, I've got to do what the hostess has planned. To-morrow I'm going to invite myself to stay home."

XIX

Seeds and Deeds

WHEN we built our house, we neglected to ask permission of the land. We pulled up its bushes and chopped down its trees and cut a gash for a driveway. We made a hideous incision in the gentle flank of the earth and brashly set our house in it, without asking permission of any kind.

Sometimes I look at the land now and wonder how it forgave us the effrontery of improvement. Yet it has forgiven. And the peace that has been brooding over it for centuries has come back to it, not as it was originally, but rearranged for us.

Hardly had we laid our rugs before we began thinking what we could do with the land. Neighbors came bringing baskets of slips and thinned-out plants, and even trees they had impetuously purchased when their houses were as new as ours.

Even Boo, who couldn't talk then, used to toddle out and bring in handfuls of weeds to plant in the bare wounded earth. We welcomed every growing thing and set it in our garden, hardly asking its name or nature. It seemed we had a nakedness of the earth that we'd never get hidden in fig leaves.

We planted and planted, anything and everything. Quantity was our only aim. It all looked raw and crude then, and unaccepted by our earth, as our very house looked unaccepted. But people kept assuring us that things would "spread," and we said, "Good. What we need on this land is compound interest."

The next year came, and we were enchanted with the quantity of vegetation. Everything sprang up, mysterious and abundant, almost rowdy in exuberance. It seemed that upon the face of the earth the multiplication table was having a field day.

It was about then we reluctantly realized that there ought to be some thought-out plan to a garden. We had all our long-legged plants standing in front of the pygmies. The delphiniums were wading ankle-deep in lobelias, and the hollyhocks spread their starched apronstrings in front of the lowly and lovely ageratums and candytuft.

When they began blooming we had more surprises and shocks. The books said blithely that no flower colors grow which aren't harmonious side by side. Maybe. But there are better brethren together than magenta and orange. Magenta, you find furthermore, is always the threat that hangs over color schemes. Magenta is the inertia-color, to which everything reverts unless care is exerted. Magenta, the line of least resistance.

And as for the things that "spread" ... well, spread is too mild a word. Gallop would be better, or gulp. For they swallow all openings and strangle all space. You pluck out basketfuls to give to newer neighbors; you tell them about the spreading, but they are young and innocent, and gluttonous for growing, and they say, "Good ... thank heaven something spreads ... that's what we need...."

But finally we all do come to the last stage of garden-civilization. From that time on, you give away no more "spreaders." You pluck them up merely to burn them, for you have learned in this simple primitive way one of the great axioms of culture.

You have glimpsed the great beauty of austerity, and you decide that nothing is worth cultivating unless it *must* be cultivated. You see it as the pattern of every-thing worth-while in human life, in education and gov-ernment, and even in love itself. At first mere having is enough. Then one comes into a higher area of appre-ciation. There "having" is only the handmaiden to serve "choosing." When one learns that the abundance of beauty is unlimited, one wants constantly less, and that less more perfected.

Our earth and we have come to this agreement now. The earth has forgiven us, and we understand each other. We are mutually considerate. We do not men-tion each other's mistakes; we forgive her weeds, and keep them controlled; she forgives our pompous plant-ings, and covers them with her grace.

Sometimes after the house has been put to bed, I walk out into the garden by myself and think about all this that I inadvertently learned, while I thought I was only planting flowers. I wonder sometimes to whom this garden belongs. I can not call it ours, for we have done grotesquely little to bring it about. Because of our own doing, not a plant-cell really came into being. All we have done is to reject the too-easy and cultivate the rare. I have not the effrontery to feel that I formed the garden; it is truer to say that it formed much of me.

For there is another Gardener of this spot, and He made both the seeds and the deeds.

It is ours only to hold. If we loosed our grasp on it for a single season, the earth would take it back to herself. Just beyond our land, the wildness waits, the loosestrife, the fireweed, the tansy and goldenrod and aster. The nameless horde is champing at our boundary lines, waiting to gallop back across our ground.

In just the same way carelessness and waste and dishonesty are waiting to overrun my thoughts, and finally the very events which those thoughts bring about. And mine they are to be weeded.

It is a ceaseless watching and pruning back, gardening. And living, too. All that is good only lends itself to you, as the land lends itself, to be built upon and guarded and watched over.

Peter, like the other fighting men who have left their homes to stamp out the poisonous weeds that have spread across our world, is learning this as he fights. Boo must learn it in her studying. Workers are learning it in their factories. It is the lesson everywhere written, waiting for the sons of men to see. God wrote it in the weeds, to wait for the needing. In the weeds and the careful-growing it stands, an indestructible alphabet of earth, and we have only begun to learn it.

XX

There Has to Be a First Time

ALL balloons are wonderful, but Cukey and a balloon are birds of a feather. Cukey is balloon-shaped, or rather he is a whole cluster of big and little spheres, from those popping-with-mischief eyes of his to his tummy.

We had quite outgrown red and green balloons in our house, but now that Cukey gives us the excuse again, we're enraptured all over, as if we have just discovered them.

Somebody sent one to Cukey in a little box, and Lilliam hoped it was a solid gold finger ring, until she got the box open and found it was only a dark little squiggle of rubber. Cukey liked it much better than a solid gold finger ring, hoping it was something he could chew. But when it was blown up, tugging and bobbing at the end of a string, he liked it better than ever. It was red and had a Mickey Mouse painted on it. He and Boo played with it all afternoon, and when it was time for him to go to bed Lilliam managed to get it away from them and shut it up in the empty bottom bureau drawer for the night.

"Balloon take the oxygen outen a sleeping-room," she said firmly. "You chillen leave me shet it up here good and safe."

In the morning, when the drawer was opened, there was only a punctured, lifeless embryo left. Cukey screamed for an hour, furious with his mother.

"Don't you cry, honey," Boo said. "I'll go right over to town and buy you another one." And she looked accusingly at Lilliam as if she had done the whole thing on purpose.

Very importantly, she managed to get over to town to make her purchase, going with Mr. Brilliant, who comes in his antiquated Packard to chop wood for us.

"How you-all gwine git past that Pointsettia comin' home alone?" Lilliam asked.

But Boo had worked that all out. "I'll walk down through the woods from the other end," she said, and her voice was saying that she'd do anything on earth for Cukey, whose mother robbed him of his treasures.

Cukey, tied to a tree, sat on the grass, waiting just as if he understood. She came slinking through the woods from the direction opposite to where Pointsettia lives, with the balloon clutched damply in her hand.

"I got it, Cukey.... Don't cry any more," she shouted, and Cukey looked at her resentfully, for he had forgotten the whole tragedy by now and was thinking about something else. "Don't cry, Cukey," she said, in a slightly deflated voice, hoping that he would, so that she could blow up the balloon and console him.

"Ugh," said Cukey and turned his back rudely.

"Look, *balloon* ..." She dangled it before him, and he snatched at it greedily, thinking it was something chewable, which is Cukey's first reaction to anything at all.

"No...you wait. You let Little Missy blow it up

for you," she said in the special sugar-voice she keeps
for him. She began to blow, and she blew and blew. I
saw it from a window, and I came out quickly.

"That's big enough, Boo," I said warningly, being
a coward about balloons, which invariably burst in my
face.

She took it away from her mouth a second and ex-
claimed breathlessly that she was going to blow it until
it was simply tree-mendous and then she was going to
snap one of our last remaining rubber bands around it,
and keep it forever.

"To show my children, after they're born," she said.

She resumed the blowing, then, and Cukey was delighted. He scrambled up on his knees and tried to
totter toward it, falling as usual and bouncing on that
rubber-ball face of his. But Boo kept blowing, huffing
and puffing, while the monstrous red sphere groaned
and shivered, dangerously huge.

"That's big enough," I said firmly.

"Just one more blow," she said between gasps, nar-
rowing her eyes and screwing up her lips for one more
gigantic effort.

Then, while all of us stared, came the bop. The ter-
rific bang. A moment of indignant silence in the air,
and all our eyes gazing at nothingness where a second
before had been the shining hugeness.

She bent over and picked up the small dark scribble
of rubber which was all that was left. She looked at it
in utter amazement.

"Well," she said. "That's the first time that ever happened to that!"

XXI

Peace Proposal

A REFUGEE child spent a night in our house, on his way to Canada. We'd have kept him permanently if we could have. For he was a revelation of ten-year-old intelligence and helpfulness. Hansli's father was a martyr who died for our cause long before we began fighting for it. Behind Hansli's dark eyes there is a surge of tragic remembering which never passes his lips. The child has wandered homelessly from place to place across the world, but now he has found a relative in Canada, and he is to settle there.

Hansli and Lisa in a room together, the child so old and tragic, the woman so young and forgetful, were a comfort you couldn't quite describe. They seemed like two cargo ships, with prows pointed toward a world we still can only guess about. They are both necessary to that world, the child to remember, and the woman to forget. . . .

Hansli went to dancing school with Boo the morning he was here. He was pleased to go, for he loved music and dancing, he said, with his funny little stiff bend at the waist.

But something went wrong in the class. At first the children clamored to dance with him, but then some youthful rabble-rouser began whispering. It was all quick and sudden, yet subtle, so that an adult might have seen it happen and not realized that anything was occurring. I might not have understood it except that I overheard the climax, for it happened in a brief skirmish behind my chair.

"Listen," Janet said, "what do you mean by bringing that foreigner here?"

"He dances better than we do," Miss Boo said.

"Yes. But he's a . . ." Janet leaned and whispered a word to Boo.

Boo looked at her in silence. "He's an American," she said.

"Maybe he is now," Janet said indignantly. "But what nationality was he born? What nationality was his father?"

"He was born the same nationality God is," Boo said, so quietly that the other child had no answer. "His father is God."

XXII

The Beamish Boy

AT four o'clock on Sunday afternoon, Miss Boo comes to grips with culture.

She looks at the clock and sits down and folds her hands demurely.

"Nearly time for Mr. Beams Taylor," she says.

She's done that Sunday after Sunday. Privately we say to each other, "I think she's going to be a musician. We'll try not to spoil it by over-encouragement."

So we didn't mention it, week after week, waiting for her to ask us for music lessons.

One thing bothered me, though. She never listens to the music. I speak of this tactfully.

"Don't have to," she says. "Mr. Beams Taylor describes it so much."

"You mean so well, dear."

"No," she says, "Mr. Beams Taylor describes it so much." She is quiet a long angelic moment, and then she says in her gentlest little voice, "When I grow up, can I take painting lessons?"

XXIII

The Letter

W<small>E</small> were on the train the first time Boo mentioned it. We were settling ourselves among the luggage, counting the bags hastily and wondering if we'd brought too much or too little.

Boo said, out of a clear sky, "Doesn't Lilliam usually ask you to read her letters when they come?"

"What, darling?" I said absent-mindedly, wondering if, in the perverse way of Nantucket weather, the temperature was going to be too warm for our light clothes, or too cold for our heavy ones.

"Usually, when she gets a letter, you read it to her, don't you?"

"Yes," I said, not realizing we were talking about any specific letter. "Don't put your elbow in those cinders on the window-sill."

The next time she mentioned it, we were running from the train to the boat at Wood's Hole. The bustling little steamer always looks as if it were going to leave you behind; you can't help running toward it, even though the time table always assures you you have eleven minutes.

"I told her you'd read it to her," Boo said breathlessly. "I said, 'She's got plenty of time.'"

"Who, dear? . . . Watch that little bag. . . . Can you

88

really carry it? ... No porters or anything these days."

We were on the boat now, and falling over the folding chairs, and wondering which side of the deck would be sunny.

"Even a short voyage is exciting," I was saying. "A train never gives you the same feeling. Don't lean over the rail too far, Miss Boo."

We watched the watercolor which is the Wood's Hole dock fade behind us, and we settled down beside the rail, and it was a real adventure, even if it were going to last only four hours.

"What kind of envelops don't have any stamps on them?" Boo asked thoughtfully. "Would those be bills? No, bills come in the envelops with windows, don't they?"

"Usually," I murmured, loving the smell of even this small harbor, and the sun on ship paint. "What letter is this you're talking about that came without any stamp?"

"The one for Lilliam this morning," she said.

Suddenly something clutched at me, but I put it aside quickly. Lilliam hadn't heard from Joseph for more than a month. ... Joseph was somewhere in the Southwest Pacific. No matter what I had tried to tell her, Lilliam persisted in thinking that Pacific was the name of a state in our Union. ("Seems lak my Uncle Henry Moakes, Momma's brother, used to live in the state of Pacific," Lilliam had said.)

"Was it in the mail this morning?"

"Yes. Lilliam took it out when she brought the mail into the house. We were already in the taxi. ... I ran back to get your mail. ..."

I remembered it all photographically. Lilliam, standing there with Cukey balanced on that jutting hipbone of hers, with a lonely look already on her face. I had called back to her.

"Boo'll come and get the mail. Just the letters . . . take out the newspapers and magazines. . . ."

I had wanted only one letter, of course—the one that reads like a telegram. "Everything fine. Tell me about Tom's baby. Is it going to be a girl or a boy?" Something like that, Peter's letter would say. Maddeningly laconic . . . and yet no matter what they said, the most precious words in the world to me.

Boo had jumped out of the taxi, and Vincent, the taxi man, had said, "Better step on it, Boo." She had run back to Lilliam, and the two of them had stood there talking earnestly until I had to open the door and lean out and call her.

"For pity's sake . . . we'll miss the train . . . we won't be able to go until to-morrow . . . get in here."

I remembered it all now, and I could even see the envelop in Lilliam's hand.

"Was it a long envelop?" I asked, helplessly far away from any definite information.

"I asked her if she didn't want you to read it," she said. "And then you said we'd probably miss the train."

I tried to quiet my sudden excitement; chances were it was only one of those semi-annual greetings which come from Lilliam's insurance company with whom I keep up such ardent correspondence, sending the sixty cents every week and then trying to get the receipt which Lilliam insists upon.

"Nonsense," I said to myself. "There's no reason to imagine it would *have* to come from the Government. It

could be anything...an advertisement probably....
People get hold of lists of names...."

As if she knew what I was thinking, Boo said brightly,
"It had the Government's name in the corner."

"How do you know?"

"I saw it," she said with the dignified haughtiness she
always feels when we question her reading. "It said
General Adjootant's office in the corner. Is General
Adjootant the name of Joseph's C.O.?"

But I knew what news it is that the Adjutant General's office sends out. I tried frantically to think of
something I could do. We were a half-hour out from
Wood's Hole now.... Perhaps I could ask the captain
to turn back the boat....

I left Boo sitting by the rail and walked around nerv-
ously. I talked to a soldier, who thought I was a little
mad, and he said yes, it *was* the Adjutant General's
office that informed families of the missing, the
wounded, or the killed.

We were the first people off the boat, and I already
had a hot handful of change ready for the long distance
call.

"Something's come up," I said to my friends in a
distrait voice. "I've got to telephone home. There must
be a phone booth somewhere here on the dock."

"But what's the hurry? Wait'll we get to our house,
can't you?"

"No. I've got to phone right away. Perhaps I'll have
to go right back home."

"Well, one thing's certain, my dear," Marian said.
"You can't go back until to-morrow. There's no boat."

The operator rang and rang our house, and nobody

answered. "She's packed up Cukey and herself and gone somewhere... the poor child... where would she go?"

I didn't tell any one about the letter, and Boo had forgotten it now. At Marian's house, I phoned again before I even opened our bags. Still there was no answer. I kept at it all afternoon, excusing myself and going upstairs every half-hour or so but trying not to let any one see that I was frantic about it.

At last Lilliam answered. "They is nobody at home, please, ma'am," she said, the moment she picked up the receiver. "Efn you'll be so kind, will you please call next Friday, please, ma'am...."

"Lilliam... don't hang up."

But she had hung up. I could see her, sad and silent, going back upstairs. The operator didn't want to ring any more. She kept saying to the off-island voice, "D.A. operator. D.A."

"You've got to keep ringing," I said. "It's terribly important." It was... more important than anything had seemed for a long time. At last Lilliam answered again, and this time, before she could say her speech, I made her understand who I was.

"Listen... you had a letter this morning?"

"Yas'm," she said. "It come in the mail, Missy."

"Boo told me. You should have shown it to me, Lilliam."

"They wasn't no time," she said. "I didn't want to onconvenience you."

"Have you read it, Lilliam?"

"No'm," she said. But it was in such a voice that I knew she didn't need to read it any more than I did. "I jes put it upstairs along with Joseph's star. God can suit Hisse'f about what He wants to do with it. It's in God's care. . . ." But I could hear her crying. . . .

"Listen. I'll hold the telephone. You run up and get it."

"Yas'm," she said meekly, and then, "But don't it cost right smart to talk on the far-away, Missy?"

"Never mind the long distance," I said. "Go get it. I'll hold the phone."

I waited then, and I tried to think clearly; I wasn't sure what I was going to do to erase the miles between us so that I could read the letter to her. Now she was back at the telephone, and I could hear the letter in her hand. I swear I could hear it trembling in her hand.

"Haven't you opened it yet?"

"No'm."

"Well, open it. And you read me some of the words. You spell them to me."

She opened the letter, and in the background I could hear Cukey saying *gruump erang* and laughing fit to kill.

"It's jes a letter. Ain't very long," she said.

"Well, spell out one of the words. Spell out the second one, Lilliam," I said, clairvoyantly trying to see if that second one was "regret."

There was a long agonizing silence.

"I cain't spell," she said softly. "Efn I could spell I could read. It's the letters I never could learn, Missy."

I remembered then that that was the peculiarity of her illiteracy. Sometimes she can recognize words in their wholeness, but never any letters. She can read her recipes because she knows the look of "sugar" and "flour" and "butter." She can read her Bible because

she knows the shape of "God" and "man" and "mercy."
But the letters are, and always will be, a mystery.

We stood apart, separated by only fifty miles of land
and the placid waters of the Sound, but I was utterly
helpless.

"Describe the letters," I said desperately.

"Well, they's a little kind of squiggle, with a tail,
and then they is a rabbit-shaped letter with its ears bent
back."

That must be a small "a," I thought wildly, while she
was going on. "Then on the next line I see that tall
biggety letter stands by itse'f . . . must be a One. . . ."

All this was too Alice-in-Wonderland . . . too hideous
with the grimness that I was sure the letter was telling us.

"Listen. You take Cukey, and walk over to the Marshalls'," I said. "You ask Mrs. Marshall to read it to
you." Suddenly I was drenched with relief, because that
utterly simple solution seemed to have spoken itself
out of the jungle of my own helplessness.

She was quiet a minute, and then she said, "No'm.
I wouldn't want anybody but my own family to know
about it, please, Missy."

I wanted to shake her, and yet . . . I knew exactly how
she felt. She and Joseph belonged to us, and this was
our own intimate sorrow. If it was to come to us, we
would bear it together, with no intermediary to read
it . . . to read the letter, and pass the word around.

"All right, dear," I said. "I can't possibly get home
until to-morrow. There's no boat until then. We'll
come as fast as we can."

"Don' you come, Missy," Lilliam said. "Ain't a thing

in the world you can do. You jes go ahead lak you planned and have you'se'f a right nice holiday."

When I hung up, I was crying. I was crying because I couldn't bear to have anything happen to Joseph, and to Lilliam. But mostly I wept because the world has need of such people as these, just to be in the presence of the rest of us so that we may learn from them.

For I know of nobody else in my world who could mean what Lilliam had just said to me, with all gentle sincerity. This is what she said as we hung up:

"Joseph would be right smart put out, efn he thought he was gwine ruin your holiday...."

I knew there would have to be a way for me to get back that night. I couldn't leave that child with the letter unread. I'd have to find some small boat, if I couldn't get a plane. I telephoned frantically. No, it wasn't possible to charter a boat any more. With the Army and the Coast Guard and the restrictions....

"I'll be right down," I said. "I've got to get on a plane somehow." I made arrangements for Miss Boo to stay with our friends, and I got over to the airfield.

"No civilian travel," the officer said, "except in matters of life and death."

"This is life and death," I said.

He was afraid to ask me if it were some one ... important. I could see him not wanting to ask, so I said, "It's some one very important." And I didn't bat an eyelash. He went into the inner office and telephoned, and waited and then telephoned again, while I sat outside in a jeep, praying. Not to my God, but to Lilliam's, who must have seen that service flag, and the letter lying under it this morning. I said, "God, Lilliam says

You're to suit Yourself about the letter. Please make it a harmless letter ... or maybe a mistake.... We need people like Joseph, God. I know You've got work Joseph could do."

After a terribly long time, the young lieutenant came out and said I could have a place in a plane that was taking an officer back to the mainland in an hour.

It was night when I got home. Lilliam and Cukey were both awake, dressed in their best clothes, and sitting in the dark in our kitchen. Not doing anything. That you could see, that is. But I knew that both of them must have been praying. For even Cukey, that irrepressible heathen, was quiet and serious. Lilliam's face had purple shadows on it, but her eyes were bright and dry.

"You shouldn't have come," she said, taking hold of my hand.

"Of course I'd come," I said, putting my arm around her. "You're ... why, you're my best friend, Lilliam."

"Yas'm," she said. "I knows that, Missy."

She took the letter out of the drawer where we keep our best silver. It had a tired look, and when I held it in my hand I knew, just as if I had been there to see it, that Lilliam had tried to match its words up to some she knew in the Bible ... or some which are her friends on the boxes on our pantry shelves. All those hours she must have matched words blindly, and prayed.

We turned on the light, and the first word that leaped out of the page was "happy."

"We are happy to inform ..."

"He's all right! Joseph's all right," I cried. "He's ... his whole company has been awarded medals.... The legion of merit, it's called." I read the words out to her, stumbling over them in my joy, and she rocked herself back and forth, and whether it was in mirth or tears I could not tell.

"Sit up there, Cukey! Listen to what your Daddy done done. Read it again, Missy."

She held Cukey upright to hear it, and he blinked appreciatively.

". . . officers and enlisted men, who have distinguished themselves by exceptionally meritorious conduct in the performance of outstanding service," I read.

"Um-*hum*. . . . That sure enough do sound like Joseph," she said, smacking her lips delightedly. And then, in a matter-of-fact voice: "What *do* it mean?"

XXIV

War Work

W E'RE all doing war work, of course. There are overalls hanging on clothes-lines in our town; lights blaze briefly at four in the morning, when neighbors come home from the swing shift.

Miss Boo quivers with impatience to be up and at it herself. War stamps are too slow, especially when you earn them by doleful tidiness in the bureau drawers. She wants something she can *do,* she says.

But lately she found it.

Janet, her rival (disrespectfully spoken of by the old folks as The Brain), is wild with rage about it. She says it *isn't* war work. And besides, Boo *isn't* doing it.

"Oh yes I yam," Boo says smugly. "And you're just jealous."

"I yam not."

"Yar so. You're jealous because you can't do it. You've got black hair."

For once Janet is silenced. She goes home and knits darkly.

You see, Miss Boo is busily growing hair for her Government. Somebody told her they need blond hair to use in fine precision instruments.

She's only got to wait until she has a hair twenty-four inches long. Then she's going to offer it to the Government.

XXV

The Way Out

SUDDENLY some one thought of the way to cure the Pointsettia situation. It wasn't Pointsettia that was wrong; it was our terrible fear of him. We'd work on that.

All we needed was to get to like dogs. . . . And then we thought of it. It was as simple as all inspirations. Of course; we'd solve it with a sure device.

"I've got some wonderful news," I said to Boo, after we'd all talked it over. "We're going to get you a little dog of your own."

"A toy dog," she said firmly. "Something like Tokay, only not invisible."

"No, a real dog. A little dog with long curly ears, and a smile on his face."

"Pointsettia has a smile," she said dubiously. "He laughs in your face."

"No, this would be different. This would be your own dog." A gentle little dog that belonged to her. Once you love one dog, you're master of all of them!

She was willing to try. We went to kennels and looked at puppies. She was enchanted. She held three of them on her lap at once, and they were better than dolls ever could be. They wiggled, and dolls only pretended to wiggle. . . .

We built him up for days. He was to be a Cocker Spaniel, born into the world for no other reason than to follow a child around. Born into the world with no other mission than love . . . to give and to have given back to him a hundredfold. He was to be fed by a child, and brushed by a child, and to be the center of a little girl's world. We had pictures of him. We got a book and became authorities on dog care.

Never was a creature so pre-loved as Frosti. From the moment we fixed the date of his arrival from the kennel, we thought of nothing else. We went shopping for his bed, and his toilet articles, his blankets, and his rubber toys. In an excess of affection, and as a guarantee of his future, we even bought him his winter overcoat. All out of Miss Boo's hard-saved allowance.

Everything in our house centered around him, those few weeks before he actually arrived. Maybe Frosti wouldn't like the dolls in the room? They'd move to the attic, and come out only when invited. Maybe Frosti would be afraid of Button Eyes, the teddy bear; off with him. Could Frosti sleep on the foot of her bed . . . just at first, until he got used to his new home? Could he have his bath in her own bathtub? When she learned to knit, would Frosti like her to make him a darling little blue sweater?

Two weeks of this, and such love generated as only a small child could offer to a puppy.

"Nobody can feed him but me," she said, "and I'll give him just what the book says. We've got to be strick. Children and dogs like people to be *strick*."

She had never called one of us by an affectionate name. Children don't call anyone "dear" or "darling," except in make-believe, when they're imitating. But she called him "Frosti-honey," when she showed me how she was going to take care of him, and she spun a continued story about their lovely life together. Happy ever after was its theme.

"And we'll get up in the morning, and I'll give him one dog biscuit, and maybe play with him a little before I go to school . . . and then he'll walk up the road with me to the bus. I'll train him to cross the road carefully, to look both ways at once, the way you tell me to . . . and then he'll sit beside the road all morning, waiting for me to come home."

The thought of him sitting beside the road, alert and watchful, thinking about her, and waiting, was joy unbearable. The dolls waited at home, while she was gone. But this was different. This waiting had a heart that rocked on a rocking-horse all day, saying, "Miss-Boo, Miss-Boo."

She had forgotten why she wanted him to walk up the road with her. Not for fear, any more, but for love. Love had cast out fear, just as the promise says. And it was not even the presence of love, but only the promise of it, more potent than any power of darkness.

Then he came. He was all he should have been, the color of honey seen in sunlight. His eyes were like golden grapes, and his ears rippled demurely down each side of his gentle little face. Nobody on earth could have helped loving him. Even people who hadn't thought about him constantly for two solid weeks.

Miss Boo herself could hardly speak, so moved was she by the sight of him. Her whole little body was pink with emotion.

"He's my very own dog," she said. "He's *mine!*"

But something terrible happened. Frosti looked at her, and saw only air. He was courteous, as all spaniels are, but totally indifferent. He glanced at me, stopped in his tracks with one forepaw lifted, and then wagged all over. He came and offered me his paw, passing the spot where Boo stood as if she were mere transparency. He looked up into my face as though he had been searching for me all his life.

"My wonderful mistress," he said. "At last. At long last we belong to each other."

I glared at him. But it didn't matter; he loved me anyway.

"My tall darling," he said, "bend down and touch me."

"He's not accustomed to children," I said to Boo. "He's been with adults. I remind him of the woman who used to feed him."

But I could barely keep from weeping myself at the look on her face.

XXVI

Time for Each Other

IT was like a benediction to have Lisa in
the house these days. A house-blessing, like one of those
hand-embroidered mottos; Lisa's presence said, "God
Bless Our Home" wherever she went. People liked just
being in the room with her, quiet and full-nourished
as a tree in fruit.

There is no sight so reassuring as a beautiful woman
waiting for her child. She is so sure of herself, so gentle
and unresisting; she is so completely at the mercy of
life; and yet, having abandoned all, she seems to have
found a safety past any touching.

She is at the same time comical and sublime. Willing
to be comical, so that she may be sublime. Both ana-
tomically and psychologically she combines comedy and
dignity in a way that art never can do. You want to
laugh at her and kneel before her at one and the same
time. She is both meek and mighty, conquered and vic-
torious. She seems to know more than a mere woman
could, and yet she suddenly has areas of ignorance and
forgetfulness and caprice that make you wonder if she
shouldn't be shut up for the duration of this event.

At a time like this, when so much in the world is
uncertain and problematic, there is a kind of cosmic
comfort in seeing the life process going on, divinely

unconcerned with petty discretion. Unhurried, unstoppable, and eloquent of law which man's tampering can not invade.

Lisa loves talking about houses and food and children. The calendar of her mind seems to have been turned back fifty years. She used to listen to news broadcasts tirelessly; she used to read all the news magazines, and argue in her clear beautiful voice; she used to know all the congressional committee chairmen and to whom one ought to write as a citizen with responsibility. But now all that is too trivial for her to care about. Now she knows about sunlight, and purées, and the best gage for cotton and linen. Now she knows recipes, and how to whiten a scorch, and that you put alum in pickles if you want them to stay crisp.

And yesterday I saw her measuring a yard as my grandmother measured a yard, by holding it at arm's length and touching it to her turned-away nose.

"How do you know such things?" I said, laughing at all the beautiful anachronism of our Lisa.

"Why . . . I don't actually know," she said, and I could see it was true. A hidden stream of woman-knowledge has bubbled up into the center of her mind now, knowledge that doesn't belong to any individual or any date. Folk knowledge . . . dating back from the time when people had children for sheer love of children. Houses were big then; all kinds of people could live in them without crowding or infringing. Two or three generations could live together in cosmopolitan harmony.

Children and pets scampered friskily around the edges of every household. Children and pets, all to be loved and played with. Houses were big enough then. Houses and hearts, in fact. Because of the old-fashioned-ness of her "condition," Lisa and all her sisterhood make you a little homesick for that time. Even though you never lived in it yourself, you feel homesick for its comfort and safety, and the bigness of it.

Everything must have been bigger in those days. Even hours. For books got read, and rick-rack got sewed on petticoats and panties, and the preserve-closet shelves glittered with jewels. Laps were bigger, too, so that children could curl up on them and be petted and sung to, while the whole room rocked in a lullaby of peace, and the whole world outside waited, kind and friendly.

It didn't "cost too much" to have a family then. It didn't cost much of anything. Only time, and there was plenty of that. Only love, and love was what the world was made of.

When you are with Lisa, you feel as if we might be getting back to such days, and you hope with all your homesick heart that we are.

For we are counting up things these days, and ap-praising them by new measurements. Some of the things which were first a few months ago have been pushed far down the list. Some of the things we had taken for granted and almost had forgotten are discovered to be the very things we are fighting for.

The arithmetic of living is topsy-turvy. Some of the things America was most proud of, the mechanical wonder-workers, can not be "added unto us" for a while. We must give them up for a time, even though they promise us greater mechanical wonders when all this is over.

I look at Lisa, and all the abundant number of women like her this year, who are going to "bring forth" (as the old Bible phrase has it) the life of to-morrow. To-morrow is going to be a difficult day. We shall all have to work harder than we ever did. Even children will have their little jobs beside us in our homes, as our mothers did, and their mothers. We shall have to make things do, and be proud and gay about making them do. Our tools will be ingenuity and cheerfulness, a new kind of pioneer skill.

It would be a divine and wonderful joke on us, if during the next years we discovered that because we have to get along without so many *things*, we should find each other . . . ourselves and our children, and all the each-others beyond our doors. Perhaps we shall find the best, because the second-bests, the "easy ways" can no longer be managed. Out of the richness of imagination and the toughness of patience, and the endurance of love, we may make a new masterpiece of living, a new high standard of living!

This is a time which hasn't any word to describe it; the fact is, there has never been such a time before. It it almost like another Genesis; a new world is being created, it seems. This time, we'll have to take better care of it, all of us. This time, we'll have to see, as God did, that it is "very good."

XXVII

Coins from the Silver Lining

A SILVER lining is usually pretty wistful optimism. In fact, the chances are, you have to find a silver lining to the silver lining, if you know what I mean. As for me, I like my silver without any cloud.

Probably there have never been so many silver linings to anything as there are to the clouds of war. Did you ever notice how often people begin cheerful observations by saying, "Well, whatever else this war has done, at least..." War credits itself with a lot of strange by-products one way and another, from getting to know the people in the next block (and riding to the war factory in their car) to discovering long-forgotten meat-substitute recipes; from not having to bother inquiring whether dinners are formal or long-dressed, to being allowed, unashamedly, to plant a vegetable garden in the front lawn.

But the amateur silver-mongers have been hard put to it to find shining linings to this almost universal business of having the people you love, and with whom you prefer to live, scattered and sprinkled about in other parts of the earth. Finding the silver in that really takes some looking!

Yet a lot of us have unexpectedly found daily coins minted from that silver. Letters. We thought we knew our family pretty well. We had heard each other's conversation over and over, the favorite stories, the do-you-remembers. They were all precious, of course, but not exciting. Not so exciting, to be perfectly frank about it, as the small talk of acquaintances. We listened with half an ear; we said "Hmn, darling? Oh, absolutely," and it didn't prevent us too seriously from doing our own thinking while we listened.

That has always been one of the reassuring things about home-folks. You can listen to them comfortably while you think about something else. A stranger, even the tamest stranger, *may* suddenly say something amazing, but those we love said the amazing things years ago, and to-morrow's surprises will wait.

We've always been so certain that to-morrow would wait! To-day didn't demand frantic attention, we thought. We've known we'd have each other sitting across the breakfast table to-morrow. But now, suddenly, to-morrow is a page we can not see, and what is written upon it we can not guess. What is written on to-day's page, paradoxically, is—absence. For we in the world who love each other most, are apart, separated by our youngness and our bravery and the fact that life is so terribly sweet to us that we would give it up, in order to keep it.

Millions of us who had grown used to each other are suddenly new. For a letter is always a view completely strange. You don't really know somebody you love until you know him by letter. Some of us had forgotten that. It's not too bad finding it out again. Things you could not say by voice, you do say in letters, gracious, well-worded things . . . thanks, particularly, and praise.

Praise is something you hope the people you love will take for granted. But when there is distance between you, you trouble to say it to each other.

Peter's unexpected, almost sheepish praise of me ... that used to be only a shy grin and a quick touch that was not quite a pat on my shoulder. My admiration of him, which I never could say to his face, can be written now, and when he comes back to me we'll never mention it. But now these are the two strands, the double-thread, so to speak, with which we sew seams so that they will not rip out, in the distance that lies between us.

Wherever we are when we open our letters, we have a family quorum. For a few minutes we are all together, the alien sky pushed back while our home-walls hold us in their own embrace.

The psychologists tell us that the only things we remember vividly are the things we have told to some one else. So the only way we can keep what we know is to give it away, and this is our time to give it away generously in letters to each other. The sunlight across his books, the dear worn chair, the silly adorable bits of nonsense we have between us—these are the small, almost tear-shaped coins we mint from this silver lining.

But all the letters, these days, are not between lovers. Now even friends must stay apart. People like Lee and me. We live only twenty miles apart, but she must pass an easel to get to me, and I must pass a typewriter to get to her. So most often we fly on the wings of a three-cent stamp.

Rarely do we write proper letters full of neighborly news, the comings and goings of events in our households. Sometimes we send footnotes to the books we are reading, or we even copy out small brilliant swatches of their fabric for each other to "feel." We tell happenings in a single line, but we go at lovely length into those inner occurrences by which congenial people discover each other, and themselves.

When I used to receive her letters at breakfast, reading absorbedly page after impetuous page, Peter would look at me and say, "Well, quite a letter from Lee! What has she to say?"

I'd look frantically for a word of "news" which might be passed across to him, and could not find a syllable. One can not say, "Well, she says to-day is hanging like a fruit against the bough of the sky...."

She paints, and can not talk; she can not even write if she realizes she is writing. But letters are different: letters are like breathing, or being grateful, or loving. Letters are like flowers; they grow into their own shape; one watches, not needing to design.

Letters between us have no pretentiousness, for we are only each other's simple journals, memos we write to remind ourselves of things we might not notice. Sometimes her letters are written on the backs of drawings, or on envelops or grocery lists. Often I turn the page and read something not meant for me...a note, perhaps, to her cleaning woman who comes in by the day: "Please do something about the rice. We're all tired of it. And the dish towels," she says.

On my side of the sheet will be something like this: "I wish I could have laid at your feet the beautiful things I've just brought into my house, because they are so full of warnings that this lovely summer is flying to its close.

"The spirit of heaviness in the headlines this spring is being put off now by the 'garment of praise.' And suddenly I see that my goldenrod and bayberries and meadowsweet are not the end of a summer, but only the beginning of different praise.

"I went that way we walked the evening you came, only I went in by the other road, through all the fragrance of the year from end to end . . . of cedar for Christmas and bayberries for long fall candlelight, of apples hanging on trees, and bread baking. My arms were full, and then my heart, and now my house is decorated for the unexpected guest.

"Thank you for writing to the discouraged man. Everything was lifted into good cheer, because somebody had troubled who has no obligation at all. The biggest happinesses are made of the smallest things!"

The world this year is full of letters. We are busy people now, and yet we find time to write our letters. We have lost some of the big things out of our life, but letters belong to the kingdom of smallest things. And we hold on to them for biggest happiness' sake!

XXVIII

No Nonsense

THE Purvises are very superior people; superior to us, I mean. They dress better than we do; they know much more than we know, and they're bringing up their child without illusions. If they have any weak spot at all, about the way they're bringing up their child, it is that they have illusions about illusions.

Alison Purvis quite often gives me little talkings-to about the way she's bringing up her child. We never mention the way I'm bringing up mine; that would not be Alison's way. So we talk about Charlotte.

"We're not going to burden Charlotte with any nonsense about make-believe and all that stuff," Alison says crisply. "Charlotte's going to be a realist, because that's what the world needs."

"Yes indeed," I say meekly, trying not to look guilty.

When Charlotte plays games, she plays spelling games, and arithmetic games. . . . She lispths through her front teeth—but that doesn't prevent her from knowing about Authralia and Athia. The joyous ignorance of other children is candy behind a shop window to Charlotte, and if she presses her little nose wistfully against the glass, you'd never suspect it from her mother.

Everything I knew about Charlotte made me determined that she'd better be protected from the necromancy of make-believe which is Boo's natural habitat. Realism, when a child is only five or six, is a very fragile cellophane. . . .

But the next thing I knew Alison wanted her to come over and play with Miss Boo.

"She's younger than Boo," Alison said, "but I think it would do them both good to get another viewpoint. I don't think she'll bore Boo at all."

"I'm sure she won't," I said confidently.

"Besides . . ." Alison looked a little apologetic. "I think Charlotte needs a slightly older companion just now."

"An older companion is often just the thing they need," I said, then and there making up my mind that the companion was going to be a whole lot older; my age, in fact. Boo would be doing something urgent upstairs that day.

Her mother brought her on the appointed day and dropped her off the back of her bicycle, a homely, square-looking child with braids; a Phi Beta Kappa in the bud, if I ever saw one.

Then, to my surprise, I found there was a third rider on the bicycle, a lopsided, bleary-eyed rag doll.

"A doll?" I asked inquiringly.

Alison flushed. "She likes it," she said. "Just a phase. Outlet for the maternal instinct. Pretty rampant at five. It gets more civilized later. Sublimated."

"Of course," I said understandingly. "At five I imagine Eleanor Roosevelt slept with a teddy bear."

Alison looked at me suspiciously, but I was so obviously trying to be helpful that she couldn't accuse me of anything.

"It's hardly the same thing," she said. "But I see what you mean."

Then she said a clipped, comradely farewell to her offspring, verbally clapping her on the back. She straddled the bicycle and prepared to ride down our hill. Charlotte watched her patiently, her guilty shame clutched to her flat, maternal breast.

"What a lovely doll," I said in the awkward pause, waiting for Alison to leave.

Charlotte looked up at me and started to say something. Then she glanced at her mother.

Alison was looking quizzically at us, as if she considered rescuing her child at the last moment from any whimsical nonsense that might be lying around loose. Then she said determinedly, "Well, cheerio, you two. I'll leave you to get acquainted."

"We three," said Charlotte, truculently, but Alison didn't quite catch it. She was on the bicycle now, pedaling out of earshot, and her sturdy back was toward us.

"Say good-by to grandmaw," Charlotte said, and held up the lopsided rag doll to wave. She kissed it rapturously, and then she smiled at me shyly.

"She's a beautiful doll," I said, noticing the way the rag doll kissed back. "Where did you get her, Charlotte?"

"She just grew out of the ground," Charlotte said in a husky voice.

"She did? How did that happen? Do tell me about it."

She looked almost afraid to try her voice. "Well . . ." she said experimentally. "I planted two lady-fingers wunth when Mother had a tea." She had convinced herself now, for she had begun with something tangible, as a good realist should. "And firtht thing I knew, she had *grew!* Right up out of the ground!"

We looked at each other in utter understanding. I suppose both our faces were a little pink. Then I opened the door of our house.

"Boo...come running down," I called upstairs. "Here's some one who wants to play with you. You're going to like each other."

XXIX

Night Time

Something terrible happened to-day. In the middle of the night our telephone rang, tearing off a ragged edge of noise across the yards of silence. It rang and rang, and every one lay stunned, and then simultaneously every one was out of beds and colliding in the hall.

It was Tom. It seemed at first he had been drinking, and then I knew he had been crying.

"Listen . . . I just thought I ought to warn you," he said. "I'm not a prospective father any more. . . ."

"Oh, Tom . . . you mean . . . ?"

The air between us hung like a choking cloud a moment, then his voice came out of it, wobbling as if one wing had been hit. "Something happened," he said. "I thought maybe I ought to tell you. . . ."

"Oh, Tom . . . where is Lisa?"

"She's at the hospital," he said, and his voice seemed steadier now, as if it had got hold of the beam again. He went on telling me about it in sound technical phrases.

"Does she know?"

"We haven't told her," he said. "But I think she knows. I saw her. . . . They just let me see her. . . . I think she knows."

"Yes," I said. "She probably knows, dear."

"I mean . . . all of it," he said. "I mean about never."

I saw by the hall clock that it was just after three. Tom probably hadn't noticed that. Time had probably stopped for him.

"Why do such things have to *happen?*" he said, with his voice cracking like a rebellious boy's. "Why does the Old Girl bring up the subject at all, if she doesn't intend seeing the thing through?"

There wasn't much I could say to him over the phone; there wouldn't have been much I could have said if we'd been together, but at least we could have touched hands, and looked into eyes.

"I'll come into town the first thing in the morning," I said. "If they won't let me see Lisa yet, maybe you and I can go to the movies or something."

"Yes," he said gratefully. "I just don't seem to know what to do."

"Well, go to bed now," I said gently.

"Bed?" he said. "Oh yes . . . bed."

When we went to the hospital, they said with that terrible, desperate cheerfulness that hospital attendants always have, that of course we could see Mrs. King. They looked at us with healthy reproach, as if it were somehow morbid of us to think maybe we couldn't.

"She'll be tickled to pieces to see you," the nurse said, showing her teeth brightly. "She's such a darling, isn't she? So *jolly,* too." I knew that her spurious cheerfulness—and her anxious mentioning of jolliness—was only her way of begging us to play this necessary game. It was decency settling as quickly as possible over a piece of realism that was too terrible for eyes to look upon. Decency . . . only trying to spare us all from knowing how thin is the vein. So I forgave her, and tried to show my own teeth, exactly as if my heart weren't lying on its face, crying.

Things move so quickly in a hospital sometimes. A lifetime is lived in a few hours, lived and let loose of, to grasp a quick adjusting. It had been only a few hours ago that all the ghastly thing had happened. But now, through the half-closed door, I could see that the room where Lisa lay was quite recovered, and tidy and smooth.

It was such a pretty room, not at all like a hospital. The bureau was shell pink, and so was the bed; a satin chaise longue waited in the window, and blue Venetian blinds sprayed creamy light over the white rugs. There were flowers everywhere, baskets and bowls and perfunctory glass hospital vases full of them. The whole room looked like a party, instead of what it was. Miss MacAfee, the toothy nurse, pushed open the door with a little ripple of beseeching mirth.

"Company, honey," she said. "That man is here again." She must have uttered that pallid jest a hundred times . . . five hundred . . . but it was her way of trying.

Lisa was propped up in bed, with her hair pinned up on top of her head, and a bachelor's button tucked bravely among the curls. I think I could have behaved myself if it hadn't been for the bachelor's button pinned in her curls.

Of all the flowers that could come to a maternity hospital, you'd never expect to meet a bachelor's button. You couldn't help wondering what kind of macabre florist would put them into a box bearing the address of a maternity hospital.

And now, to find it in Lisa's golden hair—impertinently jaunty.

I was the only one who couldn't live up to the gallant pretense. I knew I was failing them, but I couldn't help myself. The three of them, Miss MacAfee and Tom and even Lisa, all tried to rescue me from the ignominy of emotion at such a time. They pretended they didn't see those tears splashing down on my white collar; they pretended as politely as they could.

Then it was Lisa herself who tried to comfort me.

"Don't you mind, darling," Lisa said. "He'd probably have been a spoiled little beggar anyway. A nuisance to all of us."

She had a crooked smile on her mouth, as if it had been put on by a lipstick in dense darkness . . . or perhaps it was like a wry kiss smudged across her young mouth by a tragic mask. It wasn't much of a smile. But it pulled me together.

We all made a great deal, then, of the lovely room, and which chair I'd sit in. We admired the flowers; how *had* they got here so quickly? The morning sun was stabbing me in the eye, and we were awfully glad to have something concrete to do, like moving my chair around.

"Tom . . . you big oaf, move her chair, before I get up out of this bed and do it myself," Lisa said.

We did our best, Tom and I, but his fingers fumbled because he couldn't see what he was doing, either, and we nearly knocked over the bird cage, on a stand in the sunshine. Even Miss MacAfee, who must have got herself in hand permanently the very first time this

thing ever happened to a patient of hers, had to step
out of the room.

I think we all could have behaved better if Lisa
hadn't been so plucky about it. If it hadn't been *she*
trying to comfort *us*.

I kept trying to talk brightly, but all I could think of
was what a mother she would have made, when the
world needs mothering so badly. What a strong-spirited
mother, with no half-portion anywhere about her. And
now . . . never.

"Don't you two mind," she said, almost in a guilty
whisper as soon as we three were alone. "I know all
about it, and it's all right."

"Of course it's all right, darling. You're the important
thing," Tom said valiantly. "What the heck?"

Lisa looked at him and gave him a dazzling, unreal
smile. So dazzling and unreal, you knew that it was
something she had learned when they were coaching
her for her first play.

"Good boy, Tom," she said, and you'd have thought
she meant it. "I suppose they told you downstairs. . . .
I imagine they have a pep talk or something they give
the visitors before they let 'em come up. . . . I suppose
they said you were to be cheerful, and that we weren't
to talk about it."

"Not at all," Tom said in a strangled sort of voice.
"I think we ought to talk about it, Lisa. But maybe not
just to-day."

"Certainly to-day," Lisa said. "I want to talk about
it, Tom."

"Okay, then."

"It's when people don't talk about things that they get all funny," she said, but her voice had a dangerous little edge on it.

"All right. Let's, then," he said brightly.

We all smiled; we all looked expectant. I made a kind of coughing sound which I hoped was going to jar some sensible words out of me. But none came. None came from any of us.

There are some things that never have had words invented to fit them.

"Anyway," Lisa said after a few minutes, "we got that woodbox mended. Now it can go on being a woodbox, instead of a cradle."

That was so grotesque . . . so far from expressing the thing we couldn't possibly express . . . that it broke the agony into splinters. Tom let out a frightful, irreverent guffaw, and once it was started, rising in waves, he had to keep it going, for fear it would turn into a sob.

Miss MacAfee, in alarm, put her long lugubrious face around the door. Then, when she saw that everything was fine—that we were laughing—a lady-like perspiration popped out on her forehead.

"For heaven's sake, you people," she said genially. "Stop that racket. You'll wake up the babies."

That stopped him, suddenly. It left a vacuum in the moment, and it was Lisa again who rushed in to fill it.

"Yes," she said, "the babies, Tom." Then she said it again, deliberately, as if this were going to be the only time in her life she would have a chance to say those words.

"Don't wake up the babies, Tom."

XXX

Admiral Byrd

I<small>T</small> is good, undeservedly good, to come home, to come home to your own house . . . even your three-walled house . . . after a morning like this, and to find your own child, normal and safe and sound. It was good to find Lilliam in her white apron, and to hear Cukey in the kitchen, talking to himself in the unintelligible language which he speaks. I stood still in the hall and listened to the mingled sounds, and my heart budded with gratitude.

"What have I ever done that all this could be mine?" I said, and I reached out my gratitude like a hand to include Peter, somewhere in Italy fighting for us. "Dear heart . . . what have either of us ever done?" I said wordlessly to him. "Suppose we'd never found each other . . . we so easily might not have . . . suppose we'd never found all this. . . ."

Lilliam came out and looked at me, and her eyes had an anxious question, and mine must have told her the answer.

"But she's fine," I said after a minute.

"Yas'm," Lilliam said. "I knowed Miss Lisa'd be fine."

We stood there not saying anything more, and I knew that she, too, in her own way was doing just what I had done, saying thank-you-God for Cukey, and Joseph, and all this life of hers which she finds as good as I find mine. Then she bustled, the way she does, like a book turning a page.

"Miss Boo upstairs wrasslin' with writin'," she said.

That gave me something immediate to think about, for wrasslin' with writin' is something I know well. I went upstairs, two at a time, and sure enough there she was, solid and blonde, sitting at her desk with her chin on her fist, gazing into space.

"Um, writing?" I said, keeping myself from running over to her and smothering her with fierce affection.

"I've been thinking about the kind of writer I'm going to be," she says firmly.

"What kind?"

"Well," she says soberly, "I'm never going to write anything unless I want to."

I sit down beside her desk, and I unroll two paragraphs which are dismally familiar to me and to all writers. All the dreary business about discipline, about writing something every day, whether you feel like doing it or not. She listens quite quietly and then she says, with great courtesy: "But I'm not going to be that kind of writer."

"What kind are you going to be?"

"I'm going to be a good writer," she says simply.

I am staggered by that. It whirls me back to the wistful beginning, when we were all going to be good writers.

"You see," she says earnestly, "you can't write well unless you love what you're writing." Her blue eyes are honest and unafraid. I want to weep because she has said something profound and beautiful without knowing it, as a child so often does. A montage thunders across my vision . . . huge, oppressive volumes and masses of writing cascading across the weary world day after day . . . and then like the flute lilt of calmness and joy, the few winged words of grace written by each lifetime. Never any words written except those few. . . .

"I think you have to wait for inspiration," she says.

I wish then I could take back my monologue, not only from this moment, but from all the other times I have glibly uttered it. What a wealth of silence . . . what a waiting and a treasuring there would have been upon the race if only all of us had waited for the inspired words. . . .

"But what is inspiration?" I ask her, and she thinks a while. She thinks so earnestly that her eyes grow bigger, and her hands come up to the edge of her desk and seem to kneel there like two listening bunnies.

"Well . . . inspiration is where . . ." she says very slowly, "inspiration is where you look at something, and you see it more beautifully than it usually is."

Her eyes consult my face to see if I agree.

"And why do you suppose it's more beautiful than it usually is?" I ask, half-afraid to risk asking.

But I need have no fear, for she says, "Because . . . well, because you're there to see it. Wanting to tell about it makes you see it better."

It was a good definition before, but now it has in it all the subtle essence of beauty. Beauty's trinity of being, the object, the eye, and finally the word, brought back from that journey into a mental place, so that others may see it . . . more beautifully than *it* usually is.

"You be that kind of writer," I say, and then, because I am a conscientious parent, I add, with that matter-of-factness which the young must early learn to forgive in us: "But first you'd better get yourself a penmanship people can read."

"Okay," she says, matching my matter-of-factness with her own.

I went into my own workroom then, and we both were quiet, sounding like two writers from without, but within I know we both were like railway stations, with crowds jostling and trains arriving, and irrelevancies flitting past.

I was thinking about Lisa and Tom, and little Annabelle ... and wondering how I would tell Boo about it ... and remembering that I must write and tell Peter, so in case he ever had time to write to Tom ... I was thinking about the blessed ordinariness of living ... not like a play, not like a story, with everything ending properly on the last line. Things just went on, and the absurd somehow leveled the unbearable, and the inconsequential balanced the vital, and no act ever ended with a curtain line, and no curtain ever really came down.

Then our doorbell rang, and Boo redundantly came to my door, delighted with interruption.

"Somebody's at the door," she said. "I looked out the window and saw him coming up the drive."

"Who is it?"

"It's Admiral Byrd from the South Pole," she said in all seriousness.

"Oh. Well, I expected him this afternoon," I said in equal seriousness. "Tell him to park his dog sled around at the back door. I don't want the dogs pawing up the rhododendrons."

She scampered back to her room, smothered with mirth, and I went downstairs to talk to the carpenter who had come to discuss some bookshelves. He had brought his wife, a plump, cozy little woman, and the two of them, the bandy-legged little man, and the igloo-shaped silent woman, did seem to be a little on the Eskimo side.

As soon as the carpenter had gone, Boo came flying downstairs to talk them over.

"What did Admiral Byrd want?"

"He wants to deliver ice to us this summer. It doesn't seem quite practical to me, though."

She put her hand over her mouth to show she was laughing dutifully, but her eyes were still serious.

"Tell me really," she said. *"Was* it actually Admiral Byrd?"

XXXI

The Unrequited

For days Boo yearned over Frosti, and he never noticed her. He let her feed him, of course, but she was only the waitress, and she practically gave her a tip. When she called him, he turned his head, smiled politely as if she had mistaken him for some one else, and went on with whatever he was doing. He was entirely courteous, but he simply had no dealings with her.

Lilliam wanted to send him back immediately to the kennel. "He's trash," she said. "Jes onery and snubbish. Miss Boo ought snob him first. 'At's the way to git along with people like Frosti. Make out you don't see 'em *first*."

But poor Boo was too much in love for any such policy.

It was a new and terrible experience for Boo. Always before love had run out to meet her at all gates, more love than she could possibly use. If she judged from personal experience, there was no object on earth that was not made of the substance of love. But here was something, small and curly and adorable, whom she loved with all her heart ... while he simply ignored her.

He ignored her, really, because he was so diabolically

busy. Wherever I was, he kept those silly golden-grape eyes of his fastened on me. At night, he refused his lovely bed up in Boo's room. He'd start out in it, if I'd force him to, and as soon as the house was quiet, he'd get Boo's bedroom door open, by holding up two fingers and waving them frantically, so to speak. Never quite sure, and liking Boo's rug too much to take a chance, we'd let him out, and he'd dash into the darkness and disappear, watching the person who had brought him to the door, from behind a tree, no doubt, with a crafty smirk on his angelic face.

Getting back in was easy, for there was an indulgent spring on the screen door of the laundry. Then he'd creep upstairs with beating romantic heart, and in the morning when I opened my eyes, there he'd be on my yellow brocatelle chair, gazing at me with shameless joy.

So I slept with my bedroom door closed, and I stumbled over him in the morning, lying flat as a doormat, with his eye along the crack, hoping maybe he could see my feet. It was sickening, and would have been, even if there was no child in the house whose heart he was trampling on with his shenanigans.

I reasoned with him privately; I scolded him and locked him out of my workroom. He listened to the scolding and forgave me. He sat outside the workroom door waiting by the hour.

We made a grotesque illustration of unrequited love. Wherever I went, he followed me, and Boo followed him, and she was always trying to pretend the sad little procession was vice versa. I, too, did my best to make it appear that the parade was going in the opposite direction.

"Look, darling, he's following you," I'd say, whipping us all around in a right-about-face, and then bobbing out of line to make it seem I'd been somewhere else all the time. But that wolf in cocker's clothing was always right behind me, the golden goblets of his eyes spilling over with love.

"You just wait until he gets more used to you," I'd promise.

Most of the time Boo kept up a gallant pretense that Frosti knew he was her dog.

"He's so full of mischief," she said bravely. "He's always playing jokes on me. He likes to tease me. He likes to make-believe he doesn't know I'm his mistress."

Lilliam said privately, "Efn that no-good dog don' behave hisse'f, we jes pack him up and send him away. Some dogs you can't teach nothin' to."

"He's only been here a few weeks," I said. "I think he'll learn."

"Know what we do with dogs in the country? Efn they kill a chicken, we hang it around their neck, and that shames 'em so they behave theyse'fs. Whyn't we tie a string between Miss Boo and Frosti, so he'll know they belong to each other?"

But I knew that would humiliate both of them. So we went on pretending that Frosti was getting fonder of her and just not showing it much. A reticent British nature.

But one night after she had gone to bed, she couldn't pretend. Her hot little hand held mine, and I could feel it wishing my hand was a furry paw. I tried my best to make it feel like a furry paw.

"You know what I wish," she said. "I wish he'd just

growl at me once, so I'd know he knew I was his mistress."

She had reached the sad stage where she would have settled for anything, just so it came from him. But he withheld even his growls from her.

XXXII

Lipstick

I saw Lisa in Boston, several times. She had picked up everything just where she had dropped it. She had picked it up as blithely as if it never had been dropped.

The first time I saw her, after that morning in the hospital, we went to luncheon, and Lisa looked like a girl again. More beautiful than ever, and somehow smarter.

"Daddy sent me a huge check for some new clothes," she said. "Imagine Daddy sending me a check. I can't think why. Anyway I've spent every nickel of it. And fifty dollars Tom added, besides." She smiled gaily and patted her sleek hip, and in a moment she took out her mirror and looked at her golden eyebrow, and smoothed it with one fingertip.

She was full of plans. Her agent had a part for her; she was starting rehearsals immediately. It might even lead to Hollywood.

"I'm terribly glad," I said, trying to be.

She wasn't afraid I would mention anything . . . difficult. She had simply forgotten it all. She had forgotten it so completely she didn't even fear it. It was as if all the months had been a private delusion which I couldn't possibly have known about.

All the richness and the beauty, the quaintness and wiseness were gone as if they never had been, and we were both to forget them, for sane decency's sake.

We sat chatting lonesomely, and the sadder I felt the wittier I became. The more I wanted to put my hands over my face and weep, the more I laughed at Lisa's jolliness. It was our way between us of burying that beautiful lost mother who was too big to fit into this empty moment . . . too divine to be recognized in the vanity of this bereaved little face.

"Where are you, Lisa?" I wanted to cry. "All that wide spacious motherness of you must be somewhere."

When she finally did speak of it she did it in such a matter-of-fact way that I knew she was lost even farther off than I had thought.

"Have you seen Mary?" she asked, inquiring about some unimportant acquaintance as ardently as if either of us cared.

"Not since last winter," I said vivaciously.

"Yes. It was late in the winter when I saw her," she said. "Just before I became ill, I think."

So . . . it had been illness, and this poverty was health. My throat ached with pity for her. But there seemed no way I could help her.

I wanted to say, "Dear heart . . . you have created in yourself not a child, but the love of a child. . . . You must spend that love somehow. Don't let it die, when the world needs love. There must be a child for you somewhere. . . ."

But I could not say that. I could only listen to her plans, her wonderful plans, with my throat aching with pity for her.

XXXIII

Miss Boo's Husband

We hear quite a lot about him in our house. Sometimes he's very casually mentioned by Miss Boo as "of course my husband." But most of the time, he's "my babies' father." Her original idea was that she'd have several babies, each equipped with a devoted father, who'd care for it exclusively. I finally got her straightened out on the fact that she'd better count on the same father for all those fabulous babies of hers.

But whoever he is, that husband of hers, he's certainly got his work cut out for him. I try to picture him sometimes, but all I can see at present is somebody ten or so, busy with his stamp collection or his model airplanes, and not at all concerned with anything so irrelevant as his marriage to our child.

But this is the time I'd like to begin working on him, for good marriages aren't made in heaven, as we used to suppose, before so much evidence piled up to the contrary. Good marriages are made in the cradle, and at summer camp and in kindergarten and school. Some woman we don't know at all is helping at this moment to make Miss Boo's marriage either good or not, by the way she's bringing up that boy of hers.

I hope she's bringing up her son with a lot of expectations about their marriage. We think there's nothing like active, realistic expectation to make a thing—especially a subjective thing like marriage—succeed. Marriage isn't something that happens from the outside but something which becomes visible around you, a sort of shadowing forth from whatever is within.

Miss Boo has ambitions toward all sorts of professions: she is at the stage when she expects to be a lollipop manufacturer, and an airplane pilot, and a nurse, and a few other things besides. But when you discuss these aspirations with her, you find that "I" means "we," and that she pictures herself and that husband of hers piloting their big golden airplane loopily across the sky with a trail of small pink and blue airplanes following-the-leader after them, and the smallest plane, at the end of the line, will no doubt have Frosti in it...a wiser, more devoted Frosti, who loves and follows her.

She's going to "be" a lot of things, but first and foremost she's going to be one-half of an excellent marriage.

"But of course," she says, if any one questions.

And that seems very good to Peter and me. Marriage, if it's any good at all, should be something worked toward with every step you take. It shouldn't be an unforeseen emergency, like being unexpectedly called upon to make a speech on a subject you've never heard of.

Sometimes when I see her playing her complicated "house," I meditate on what I'd like to give her for a husband if I were able to. I'd like him to be brought up without illusions. Illusions seem egotistical criticism against God Himself. For illusions say that we, finding the world intolerable as it is, have created a make-believe world. The world as it is...even as it is at this moment ... is *not* intolerable. It is beautiful and great beyond any measure. But it is unfinished, and always will be. It is on its way to becoming better, and we are here to help it.

I think children should be told the truth about the world. About everything ... as fast as we can find the truth. Only the short view of the world is discouraging. For if we've learned anyhing at all in the ten million years we've had a world, it is that things finally get better. The more you develop what is already good, the faster the whole gets better.

If it were within my power, I'd like to see that our child marries into a family of happy people. Never mind too much about their finances, or their ancestry. But we can not graft our merry child upon any family tree which is a weeping willow. Unhappiness ... chronic unhappiness ... is a sin against life. We know quite soberly that catastrophes may happen, bitter and over-whelming things. But nothing that can happen—and this is written at the bedside of the illest world imaginable—must ever be considered as justifiable excuse for a disspirited and misanthropic race, or individual. Whatever happens, we dust ourselves off, and go on. We do that now when we fall off a seesaw, and intend that that shall be the pattern of behavior, large or little.

Maybe the world contains so few conspicuously happy people because we learn too late exactly what happiness is. It is no accident, no magic coincidence. It is a condition of adjusted balance. It isn't a state at all, in any static sense, for happiness is not a station you arrive at, but a manner of traveling. Happiness is a habit, to be established early. It is like the magnetic beam by which the pilots fly.

I hope that son-in-law of ours knows how to laugh. I don't doubt he arrived in the world laughing; they all do. But soon they model their expressions from us. I hope he is noisy and exuberant, for these are the husbands we like. (In fact, I imagine that if he is a lugubrious, solemn chap, he'll never even cross our way. He'll pull down his hat over his ears and hurry off on the other side of the street.)

There is another kind of laughter we want him to have. It is the subtlest laughter in the world, and I do not know how it can be taught except by divine contagion. It is the love-laughter which can be shared only by two people in love. People laugh only when they are well, and love laughs only when it is very well. We used to hear it when we were children, when our blue-eyed Welsh mother and our stern Swedish father were alone. In all the thirty-five years of their married life, I never heard one call the other "dear." It was too deep for that. But they had jokes in a language we couldn't know, and sometimes in the night we'd half-wake and hear them laughing behind their bedroom walls.

This husband of Miss Boo's must enjoy many different kinds of things. Work, first of all. And then various skills about which she can boast, and outdoor crafts. I hope he has holiday talents, for one of the saddest sights on earth is adults enjoying themselves on holidays. Fun is something you *have,* not something you watch.

I hope he can apologize. I hope he can be sorry quickly when he has been wrong, and can say so generously (and even sometimes when he hasn't been wrong). Apology is a lovely perfume; it can transform the clumsiest moment into a gracious gift.

His mind, I hope, will be amused with itself. And his body, I hope, will be tidy, and his habits wound and set by a clock. But if he *is* tidy and punctual, I hope he won't be too intolerant of the rest of us, who are only *trying* to be.

He'd better like children, for Miss Boo has been covering things with blankets since before she could talk. She mothers everything, including caterpillars, fallen leaves, older children, and me.

In the midst of asking such a lot from that unknown woman who is training a husband for our child, I can not help wondering if she will be satisfied with what I am doing toward that marriage. It is difficult to know what to teach children to help fit them for the strange, unpredictable world which is even now emerging from chaos. Our parents could give us educational dimensions, social location, and financial predestination, of a sort. But, if we face facts at all, we know we can not guarantee any of that to our children.

What we can give them are only the things which nobody can take from them—only themselves, and the ability to be at home in the world. Not any way of life, really. They must find their own way of life in the new bare world.

We can give them themselves and the pioneer legacy of certitude that that is enough. Good, tough, clean bodies, and minds large and resilient, from which to make everything necessary, laughter and love, and building and being.

That is basic equipment, and it sounds a little grim to us who have leaned so much on what is outside—prestige and privilege and background. Yet there is audacious freedom about it which we have never glimpsed. Only big and daring people can face the dangers our children must conquer—people who don't have to reach far outside themselves for instruments and tools.

I get a bit pompous when, even in my imagination, I become a mother-in-law. (He'll need a sense of humor about me, you see!)

Miss Boo, whose business it is, after all, is much more practical about it.

"You know what?" she says. "How would it be if I married a taxi driver, and then we could always *get* places."

XXXIV

Grace for This Day

I DON'T quite know how it started. Maybe because the news broadcasts come immediately before dinner. But anyway, before Peter went away, something began happening in our house. Some unseen presence came in, and after we had listened to the news, it took us each by the hand and led us more quietly into our dining-room.

The first time we felt it, we had no words.

The second night one of us said with embarrassment, "Funny thing. Don't laugh, but just now I had a feeling we were all going to bow our heads and say Grace."

"Grace?"

"Yes. You know, that old-fashioned custom of giving thanks before a meal."

Then Peter said, "I *have* been giving thanks. Every time I see our table, and us around it, and good food upon it. I say it to myself."

"Let's do it together."

So that night we did. Later we learned words to say together, but that first night we said our Grace in silence. I didn't know any formal words, but something in me said, "When danger walks outside the house, those within become reverent. . . . Forgive us for that spiritual mercenariness, please." And Something answered, "There is nothing to forgive. Only draw near to Me."

By family agreement we didn't mention it to each other, and when guests were at our table, we forgot it entirely. It seemed such an old-fashioned thing to be doing in this modern world ... people might not understand ... and anyway, it was really only our own business.

A few nights ago we were invited to a neighborhood dinner at a house half-way down our hill. It was quite different from the dinners we used to have. For one thing, we all brought our children, for there's no one to leave them with now that the factories have called most of our maids.

There are gaps in almost every family, and we carry letters from strange places to read to each other. Several of us have filed-down fingernails which mean we work in a war factory, and two of us must break away early to go on the night shift. But the little time we have together is spent hilariously, for we appreciate it as we never did before.

Just after we sat down at the table, there was a moment's pause. I thought guiltily that it must be my fault or Boo's. Then I saw it was nobody's fault. It was something that sprang from each of us, a still expectancy. It became awkward, for we are unaccustomed to such awareness, and we have not yet found words for it.

"Guess we might as well say Grace," one of the men muttered. "Seems appropriate these days. For everything we have here ... and what we intend to do with it ..."

We bowed our heads, and somebody murmured some

ancient words. But all of us were saying our own Grace in our own way, childish and wise, grown-up and simple. Probably Miss Boo was saying, "Umn ... I smell duck and sweet potatoes. ... Dear God, why don't you send my share to the children in Europe? ... Please take care of them, God. Amen."

I think I said, "Thank you, God, for this family, and this town. For every day of them. Please take seeds from this happiness of ours, and scatter them across the world. ..."

All of us were saying Grace for food ... and for more than food, even lovingly prepared, even beautifully served. We were thanking God for something bigger. For America herself, and for what she means in hope to a frightened world. For her vast table-lands of wheat, her orchards cradled in the New England valleys, her neatly combed miles of beans and carrots, and the tall troops of corn marching in phalanxes across the center of our map.

We were not just one little neighborhood at table; America herself must bow her head and say a Grace by being merciful in bounty.

XXXV

Ballet in the Morning

ONE morning quite early I looked out of our window, and there among the trees was an elfin pantomime. An animal often becomes fay when it plays alone, not knowing it is watched by any human eye.

There was a little knoll where the sun through the leaves made a kind of spotlight, and Frosti was dancing upon it. He was chasing something invisible, touching it with his curly paw and leaping away from it. He was waltzing on his back feet, with his long ears whirling about his head, laughing to himself, like a faun in a ballet. Round and round he went, while the tiny stringed orchestra of crickets and katydids, and waking birds made a silver haze of sound over it all. The trees shifted overhead, turning the sunlight from gold to green and back again to gold. Shadows of leaves danced with him and leaped across his tiny stage, clasping him mischievously and then running off.

He danced and spun, and when he tired of that, he curled up and made a hassock of himself, and lay dreaming, while the corps de ballet of shadows did intricate figures over him, or trembled in spirals of *entrechats*.

There was an audience to all this. As quiet as an audience should be. It was Pointsettia, sitting ten feet off, alert and admiring. When he came over and asked humbly if he could play, too, Frosti stood up and turned his back and lay down again. Pointsettia, gentle and rebuked, went back to a respectful distance, sat down on his haunches, and continued to watch.

"Why, he's a beautiful thing," I cried to myself, and I wasn't talking about the ballet dancer but about the tall, gentle watcher. "He's like a silver image sitting there. . . ."

But that vain little Frosti was making him transparent in the air, just as he made Boo negligible.

It happened several mornings, before the house was awake. It wasn't art on Frosti's part, of course; he simply loved the morning sunlight on his golden coat. Then one morning, to my amazement, I saw a little figure, wrapped in a pink bathrobe, stealing out through the trees and standing just as Pointsettia was standing, alert and humble and adoring.

I wouldn't have listened to what they said to each other, the three of them, even if I could have heard, because it was their business and none of mine.

But Frosti showed that he could ignore two people as easily as one. Once, when Pointsettia came too close, walking stiffly on his long legs, Frosti took a nip at his ear, and then royally included him in the exclusion. He played about by himself, whirling and prancing and snarling at imaginary prey hidden behind clumps of leaves, but when either of the two watchers approached to join the game, he curled up and went to sleep.

Boo, her heart obsessed by her hopeless passion, forgot she had ever been afraid of Pointsettia. She sat down beside him, and the two looked very much alike, the bony, stilt-legged dog, and the wistful rejected little girl, both with their faces turned toward something that just wouldn't care.

When Pointsettia's front legs got tired of being braced, he let them slide out in front of him on the slippery pine needles, and then he moved an inch nearer to Boo and put his long head timidly on her lap.

For a second she looked startled. For a second, I thought she was going to leap up and run screaming into the house. And I think she would have if there had been a grown-up near. But then, from the window, I saw her whole body grow fluid in line, and her hand came up and patted Pointsettia's head. She had wanted a dog's head under her hand for such a long time....

Then she bent over and kissed the top of his head. But Frosti just turned his back.

XXXVI

A Job for a Child

I DREADED Lisa's coming to our house. I wanted to see her, of course, but I dreaded it. I knew before it would be safe to have her that I must somehow manage to tell Miss Boo about Annabelle.

"I'll tell her casually, sometime when it falls just right," I said to myself. "I'll say something like 'Oh, by the way, darling, when you see Aunt Lisa, I shouldn't say anything about...'"

I knew it would be difficult to make it as casual as that. Like many difficult things, I put it off until it was too late. For Lisa didn't wait for an invitation; she came one day without warning.

"I just popped out," she said brightly, "in case Turner sends for me in such a hurry that I can't say good-by to you people."

Turner was pretty sure he had something good for her... wasn't that splendid?... It might take her through the winter.... Tom would get along fine, of course. It seemed as if Tom had buried himself in his classes more than ever this term.

She didn't ask for Boo; though she hadn't seen her since the last Sunday before the hospital, she didn't mention her at all. I kept wishing that Boo was away somewhere, where there'd be no risk of awkwardness. "I should have told her," I kept thinking guiltily. "This ought to teach me a lesson."

I knew Boo would come bursting into the room, the minute she heard Lisa's voice, and the first thing she would say would be . . .

Then I heard them out playing under the trees. She and Cukey and two children from down the hill. They were playing some kind of game. Cukey, of course, plays by sitting and watching. He's an actor who speaks any part, and they all write his rôle as they go along.

"Cukey's the captain, and Cukey chooses me on his side," Miss Boo says, having at last solved the problem of getting her way by a majority vote. Cukey screws up his eyes and laffs fit to kill. Cukey shakes his little head and scolds, and his eyes rattle around in his face like two black-and-white dice in their box, come seven come eleven.

It seemed to be one of those "choosing" games they like so well. You choose between two wonderful alternatives, and if you choose the glass playhouse, you're on one team, and if you choose the pink marshmallow palace, you're on the other.

It was Boo's turn to choose, and I could hear her being excited about it, while the other children dawdled in suspense.

"Which would you rather have?" Joanie says and then pauses dramatically.

"Go on . . . go on . . ." Boo cries in excitement.

"Which would you rather have: A solid gold chariot with diamond headlights . . ." Joanie drools with the gorgeousness.

"Or what? ... Go on."

"Or a beautiful coat made out of white fur?"

I can hear Boo thinking and thinking, and Cukey saying "Ugh," and not influencing her one bit.

"Let me name my own," Boo dickers. They argue a while, and Lisa goes on pretending we are not listening in this room. Lisa lights a cigarette.

"You're smoking again?" I ask. "I thought you'd stopped."

"Oh, that ..." she says scornfully. "Some nonsense of the doctor's while I was ill, I guess."

Then Boo's voice rises triumphantly. "I tell you what I choose," she is shrieking. "I choose lovely little twins. A girl and a boy, with patent leather dancing slippers and lovely straight hair."

Lisa and I both start to say something at once. Anything. Then we stop, and beg each other's pardon, and both don't go on. ...

Lisa is out of her chair now, blindly examining some flowers which Lilliam put on the coffee table this morning when she dusted. Lisa has one flower ... a pungent chrysanthemum undaunted by the frost ... in her hand. She has crushed it in her hand, and I can smell the bitter camphor fragrance of it.

"Lisa, listen ..." I try to say, and she shakes her head so violently that I know she can not bear to have me talk about it.

"No," she says. "No." Then she laughs. "That Boo of yours," she says unsteadily. "Always picking twins for people. She's incurably maternal, isn't she?" She tries to smile at me, to show me that it is *not* unbearable at all. But her mouth is quivering, and she gives up the attempt. "Anyway, I tried," she says in a whisper. "Nobody can say I didn't try, can they?"

Then she gets hold of herself, and she sits down and looks straight into my face. "This is silly," she says sternly. "You see, I really am glad, now that the whole thing is over."

I want to say, "No, you're not, Lisa," but I dare not.

"No use fooling myself about it," she says, and her voice is as crisp as the chrysanthemum ripened by the frost. "I'd have made a heck of a mother. The Old Girl knew what she was doing. I'm an actress, not a mother."

I want to say, "Maybe to some people, Lisa. But to me you're not a very good actress." But I dare not say even that. For, good actress or not, she's a very gallant one.

She has new lipstick on now, and she is quite recovered. She gets up and looks in the mirror over our fireplace. She smooths her hip, as if that were an argument in itself.

"I must go out and see Miss Boo. I've got to make a train back to town in an hour or so."

I protest, of course. She'll have to stay to luncheon; Lilliam would be hurt. . . . But she insists. There's a train in thirty-five minutes, and she's got lots to do back in Boston; she always has so much to do. . . .

She made her train. I couldn't keep her. Not even Lilliam's spoon bread and honey could keep her. Miss Boo walked down to the station with her, and they were laughing when I watched them out of sight.

It wasn't until I saw Boo coming back, walking very slowly up our drive, with an absent-minded spray of milkweed pods in her hand, that I remembered I had intended to protect Lisa from being alone with Boo.

"Aunt Lisa get off all right?" I said unnecessarily, the way people do when some one's gone to the station.

"Yep." Boo sat down on the grass and watched a spider bustling around at his engineering.

"Nice seeing her, wasn't it?" I said invitingly.

"She's my favorite aunt," Boo said passionately. "Of all my aunts."

"She's mine, too. Of all your aunts."

We look at each other, and both of us recognize the terrible weight of love we feel for Lisa.

"Did you talk about anything special?" I ask.

"Of course," she says, prodding the spider.

"Annabelle?"

"Of course." What else *could* one talk about, her eyes say glowingly as they meet mine, and then return to the engineering.

"Annabelle isn't going to be born this year," she says softly. "She's changed her mind about this year. But she *is* coming . . . later."

"She is, darling?"

She looks up into my face, and her own is so beautiful and earnest with trying to make me understand that I can not tell which of us is the child and which the older one.

"Annabelle's going to be born to somebody else . . . but she's going to belong to Aunt Lisa," she says. "It doesn't matter *who* a child is born to, really. It's the people she belongs to that's important."

"Did . . . did Aunt Lisa explain that to you, dear?"

She thinks a while, with her silver eyebrows puckered.

"We explained it to each other," she says at last.

XXXVII

The Gift

It was fall now. The house grew snugger, and we all drew closer to each other, as people do when the world grows cold.

The apples came in, chilly-cheeked and fragrant, to be sorted for winter evenings when the fire blazes and the book still has a two-inch stack of good pages waiting under the right thumb.

The cordwood is a stout bivouac beyond the dooryard, and popcorn hangs in the attic. There are plaid skirts folded in Miss Boo's bottom drawer, and flannel pajamas (no feet on them now ... but grown-up pajamas that look as if they might be enrolled at Vassar).

The pencils are sharpened, and last-year's eraser is found at last, since we can't buy a new one. To-morrow Miss Boo will be starting back to school.

She has pictured the moment a hundred times. Early in the summer, when she painted it in, she saw a devoted little spaniel gamboling beside her as she went up the road. But Frosti is still indifferent and aloof.

During the last two weeks, she has worked especially hard at winning him over. Pointsettia has worked, too. Pointsettia is suddenly adolescent. His wild galloping through the woods is over; he is pensive now, and almost shy. He comes and sits docilely on our boundary line.

hoping Frosti will invite him over. But when he comes without invitation Frosti yaps at him, and Pointsettia is too much of a gentleman to answer back to such a small fluff of impudence. Pointsettia, so much too big to meet Frosti as an equal, has the disadvantage which the chivalrous strong always must show toward the arrogant weak.

Boo, knowing all too well how he feels, tries to comfort him.

"Don't you mind, Pointsettia-honey," she says. "He's going to play with you. He's just not used to you yet."

Pointsettia, in return, licks her hand and says what he can to help her. They understand each other perfectly, two rejected admirers of something unworthy and desirable.

The night before school opened, when I put her to bed, she said: "You know what I think? I think Frosti is going to surprise me to-morrow. I think he's going to be waiting to walk up the road with me to the school bus. He knows that's why we got him. Don't you think so?"

A child needs a dog. And I have done my best to give our child one. But there are some gifts which can not be given. That is one of the most difficult things a parent can ever learn. Some gifts you would break your heart to give, and yet you can not. For a gift must be drawn; it never can be pushed from without.

Lying awake, worrying about to-morrow, I thought of all this, and I wondered if God Himself must have had to learn that hard lesson of love, when He yearned to give us what we didn't accept.

But the analogy was somehow out of joint, and I was half-asleep and couldn't straighten it out.

Then, in the morning, it straightened itself out, and I saw the meaning, the human one and the divine.

Sometimes the gift we so urgently offer is not the best ... only the second best. But the right one waits until it is taken. Such are the gifts of God. His giving is so wise, it must always wait for our accepting.

In the morning when she started out with her pencil box and her clean handkerchief, Boo had her dog to walk up the road with her. That morning and every morning from then on. To walk up the road with her, as she had pictured it, and to wait half the afternoon for her to come back.

Boo has her dog at last, the proudest thing in our neighborhood, and the most protective. And what he is protecting her from, they have both forgotten.

Boo has her dog at last, to play with and to love. But it isn't Frosti.

XXXVIII

The Seed in the Apron Pocket

W<small>E</small> have known each other a long time,
Mrs. Novatny and I. It seems like forever, but when I
count up, it is only six years. They have not been ordinary years. We each have crowded a lifetime into them,
and the world has crowded an eternity of sorrow.

I found her little grocery store on a side street in our
town. The store is really a house, with its front windows
bulging out over her little dooryard. There is a bell
attached to the door, so that you enter to chimes. And
Mrs. Novatny comes from behind a flowered curtain
that discreetly shuts the shop from her parlor, with a
smile on her face, and suds on her hands, and the earrings in her pierced ears, twinkling. I used to think up
errands so I could go in and talk with her, for I knew
our friendship would progress at a dignified pace, slow
and tried at each step, and I wanted to get on with it.

Old-fashioned dried peas, ice-cream salt and potato
flour, and a square candy jar of dill pickles sit side
by side on her shelves. To me the shop smells faintly
of kerosene and sawdust, but I think that comes from
my childhood memory of little stores like hers.

We never had a great deal to say to each other, but
we got acquainted, and once she gave me a box of Czech
Christmas cookies with hard pink sugar glittering on

the tops, and once I took her children to the circus. She showed me her garnet earrings, which she keeps in a chamois bag, with the gold-framed miniature of her family.

We were friends from the inside out, not from the outside in, so we did not need many words, or many things in common. Not many small things, anyway. And the big things we have in common require little talking about.

Once I helped her write a letter home. She wanted it in English, partly out of wistful boasting, partly out of sheer love of her new tongue. Though she had pored over her husband's night-school books, she could not find what she wanted to say. I could not find it either, for I have no words for such ardor and pride and gratitude. She wanted all of America to go into that letter— her fence with the hollyhocks, her washing-machine, the little church she adores, the bus trip she took that summer.

"Fields and fields of food growing, like heaven!" she said to me, sitting with her knees hugging each other and her bony fists clasped with earnestness.

She wanted them at home to see her children's clothes and their school.

"Tell them like a palace, so big. With a place to swim," she said.

She wanted to tell them about the excellent hospital where her baby was born.

"Not in the bedroom at home. Tell about the hospital and the nurses, looking as if brides," she wanted me to say.

She wanted them to taste American strawberries, and

to peep into her husband's pay envelop, and to know his boss, who calls him Buddy and slaps him on the back.

She wanted a word for all of it, to sum it up. The only word I could think of was "freedom," but she said that was a word they wouldn't know in Czechoslovakia. Even then—four years ago—they would not know it, she said, as we know it here.

During the next days we pictured that letter arriving, and the priest or the school-teacher translating it. It was more than a letter; it was a little spot of America, on which those people might stand a moment holding freedom in their minds, and so becoming a little free themselves. . . .

I saw war come to her face. I read about war in my newspaper, but when my heart tried to understand it, Mrs. Novatny's face was what I saw. Winter was in her face, and no words of mine could melt it.

"Iss so bad," she said, and I nodded.

Head-lines threshed across her country, cutting down one unpronounceable town after another. Head-lines picked up her own town for a day or so and then dropped it into the abyss of tragic oblivion. I saw in her face that she knew. When we could speak of it, after a while, I saw that she had lighted an almost-preposterous torch of hope about it.

"They are well, my little brothers and my mother," she said. "I feel it in here, they are well. They will come to me some time in America."

"Yes."

"Letters can not come," she said confidently. "But I will hear some time."

Then, last Tuesday, she heard. A flier, escaped from her town to England, had come to Canada for instruction. He had known Mrs. Novatny when they were children at home. So he brought the word, the full terrible word.

Boo brought it home to me. "The Novatny children aren't in school," she said, as if she knew this were no ordinary staying-home. "A letter came for their mother."

To-night I went to her side door. The little shop was closed, the blinds were drawn. It was a strange house of grief, for there was no beloved body to mourn over. It was death, bigger than any body. Bigger than any single body. As big as the world itself.

She opened the door, and I tried to find some word, but I could only touch her hand. Her eyes looked at me courteously with their ancient race-wisdom.

"You are a child," her eyes said, "all of you in America, happy heedless children, safe and extravagant and noisy with your fun. You can not know what *this* is like, my child."

She tried to say something to show she appreciated my coming. "Iss cold," she said gently. "Iss cold... everywhere."

The zinnias in her garden were dead. She stepped down from her porch and took a handful of seeds from the brittle heads and put them in her apron pocket. She didn't know she was doing it; it was an old instinctive gesture.

I stood there wondering how I could make her see that that gesture has something to do with her lost country—with all the lost world that must live again, the laughter and loving, the trusting and hoping. But I could find no words.

"Czechoslovakia iss my body," she said. "Chains on her make bruises into me."

America is *my* body, but the chains in Europe make bruises on my life, too. Nothing that I know can be the same to me until the world is free again. Nothing.

To-night when I look out of my window down into our valley, there are lights in new factories. It has all happened so quickly it still seems like a scene in a play. But it isn't any play; it is sober, terrible intention, and nothing is going to stop it.

Almost every house in our town has a factory worker in it. I hardly know my own house, because of what has come into it and what has gone out of it. But I would not have it any other way.

These are the words I could not find to say to her ... these factories, this house ... multiplied by all the vastness of America. We might say it is our promise, only it isn't so vague and wordy as any promise about to-morrow. It *is* to-morrow itself, the very substance and bone of to-morrow. As many to-morrows as are required to wipe this war from the earth.

And we will wipe it off, however long it takes. I know that. I know it by those tired streams pouring into the factories. And I know it by the very thing in me which makes me want to tell all this ... and by the very thing in a grieving woman which, though withered by the world's most bitter blast, made her stretch out her hand to put seeds for another spring into her apron pocket.

XXXIX

The Happy Beginning

W<small>E</small> all go on, making the most of our small
sweet pleasures: Cukey's new tooth, Boo's perfect spelling paper, and the fine notices Tom mails us from Lisa's
New York opening.

The news in the world is better, but I read it with
tightness in my throat, for there has been no letter
from Peter for a long time. The last one came from
Italy, but not the Italy we knew together once. There
has been nothing at all for five weeks and three days,
and I am certain he is dead, and I go around with my
mouth bent in a smile like a wire. Wondering what
will happen to us ... thinking nobody could possibly
know that I am worrying, under all my gaiety.

But for each other's sake, all of us worried women
across the world, we keep on. We even make a kind of
nourishing happiness out of these days. It is not exciting; it is a kind of bread, but it is good bread. The
uneventfulness of the present we cherish, because our
lives lie in the shadow of too-much-happening. We are
glad when nothing happens....

But the other evening, just after our dinner, something did happen. By telephone.

First the nasal impersonality of the operator, asking
our number in a querulous voice, and then the usual

one-minute-please, and finally, "Springfield is calling."

"It's probably a wrong number," I said to Lilliam, who had come dashing upstairs to say far-away was calling. "We don't know anybody in Springfield."

But I could see by the fear in her face that she had made an instantaneous connection by a series of short circuits and coincidences which made it plausible to believe that bad news was coming about Joseph. Her face was already on its knees saying its prayers, having faith and fear locked in a struggle.

"Nonsense," I said to her—and to myself, whose terror had gone in step with hers. "No news would come through Springfield."

"Ain't Washington got somethin' to do with Springfield? Kind of a suburb, ain't it?"

"Washington's got something to do with every place," I said grumpily. "Just stop worrying . . . yes, hello . . . this is she . . . what?"

And then there was Tom on the wire.

"Hey, you-all," he was shouting so loudly that everybody in the room could hear him.

"You don't need to tell me," I said, while he was swallowing from sheer excitement. "You've found him . . . or her . . . or something. . . ."

Then there was a tangle, and Lisa and he were fighting over the phone, and Tom was saying, "Go away, you said I could tell 'em." And Lisa was saying, "Now Tom, don't be silly. . . ." And neither of them was telling me, and neither of them had to.

"But why Springfield?" I was shouting, just in order to start with something concrete.

"She's a native of Springfield . . . at least she's not a

native of any place, yet . . . she's only three days old . . ."
Tom was saying, and then Lisa finally got hold of the
phone, and she said:

"Darling, this madman has become a father after all."
Her voice had stars and asterisks all around it. "Dr.
Buck telephoned me unexpectedly. I'm giving up the
play, of course . . ."

Then Tom: "She's a little girl. She's . . . beautiful . . .
looks like Lisa . . . honestly she does." His voice was
off the edge of the telephone.

"She doesn't yet, of course," Lisa said, trying to be
honest. "But Dr. Buck says that often they really do
grow to resemble their parents in time."

We all babbled on then, and the operator came in
and mentioned three minutes, and Tom said, "Oh, go
away," as if she were a mosquito, and went right on
talking and talking.

I knew the last sorrow was gone when Tom said:
"This is the way to have babies, no foolin'! Gives both
parents a chance to sit outside in the hospital waiting-
room together. The poor old father doesn't have to bear
the whole thing by himself."

So, a baby had been born to them at last. Not cir-
cumstantially of their bodies, but desirously of their
hearts. They had both borne this child, as Tom had
facetiously said; they had looked for it and waited,
looking and looking until at last they found their own.
They would be a good family, with a child doubly dear,
because of itself and another.

I looked around our room, so precious and helter-
skelter and full, with Boo lying on her stomach in front
of the fire. Her book was forgotten because of the baby,

and I wished with all my heart I could know what she was thinking.

I was wondering, for the thousandth time, why people live without children. Sometimes I look at the tight, frightened, shrewd faces of strangers, and I think how much the world needs the nourishment of love. The well-loved faces stand out, rich or poor, like grapes among raisins.

"I knew they looked like mothersnfathers," she said at last, going back to her book, well-satisfied. Yes, after all these months, I see that she was right; they had the look of mothersnfathers ... and it should be one word.

I remembered something my mother used to say: "You can know when God lives in a house if you hear laughter when you open the door." You can know, too, when you look into a stranger's eyes, if they have looked intimately into children's faces. For there are things which only a child can bring into a face, and into a life.

XL

Wonderful Things Happen

Sometimes on Saturday night, when Lilliam is stuffing the chicken for to-morrow's dinner, I go in and sit a few minutes with her, and we sum up the week.

To-night I am happy with no pretense. For this morning my letter came. I know every word of it, every blot; it says nothing particular, but it says enough, and for me the world is sound as an apple again.

I have not mentioned the letter, of course. If my house is not to sag and droop between letters, it is imperative that I make no more of their coming than of their not-coming. We have learned, we people waiting at home, to hold our peace. It is a wonderful phrase: to hold our peace. We hold it firmly and gently; we hold the worry and the relief equally hidden.

"Us gwine have sweet potatoes and cohn puddin', and I'se gwine open up one of my pickled peaches," Lilliam says, expertly spanking the chicken with her own blend of seasonings. "Us gwine eat good to-morrow."

"Us always eats good," I say.

"People kin eat good no matter what," she tells me. "Makes no matter efn they only got hominy grits an' greens. Cook 'em good, and eat 'em with a good heart, and they is *good*."

We talk about Cukey a while. Do I really think that is a word he say this morning?

"It sound lak a word," Lilliam tells me, trying to be honest about it. "But it don' sound lak a word I'se heard before."

Cukey is nearly a year old now, and Lilliam has decided that she's not going to put pink hair-ribbons on him any more. And maybe no more vanilla dashed behind his ears when he's dressed up.

"I sure lak a chile that smells *good*," she says. "He kinda cute-smelling with vanilla on. That Cukey."

We chat along about one thing and another. I try to explain the reason why the letter "p" is "d" upside down, for Lilliam is mastering the alphabet at last. Mastering is hardly the word; she is arguing with it. So far neither of them has given an inch. But by the time Cukey is four I think she will know the alphabet, and she will teach it to him. That is the plan. And then if she isn't ever able to learn to read, Cukey will never believe it, efn in case anybody ever accuses her of it, in his hearing.

"Cose she kin read, efn she desires," Cukey will say, according to Lilliam's prediction toward this distant moment, twenty or thirty years from now. "I extinctly remember she taught me mah alphabet, when I was a little bittie boy."

So now we are at "p," and it is just ignorance on my part that I can not at the moment produce the reason it is "d" standing on its head with its back turned.

"Well, nevah mind," Lilliam says forgivingly. "But

efn you do think why that is, you tell me, please, ma'am."

She goes on fluffing up the stuffing. Heavy chicken dressing, she says, is pushed down; hers she fluffs *up*. She smiles as she works—not a smile you could say was on her mouth really. It is a smile of presence, really, an aroma of contentment that makes you grateful for your whole house, as you sit in her kitchen with her.

"This here's been one of my best weeks," she says. "I'se had three wonderful things happen to me."

This surprises me, because I've not heard of anything at all happening to Lilliam. The good happenings must have come tiptoeing in, when I was looking the other way like the letter "d."

"Yas'm. Wonderful things done happen to me *this* week," she says thoughtfully.

"Did they, Lilliam?"

"Yas'm. Sure did." Then she looks at me in surprise that I could have forgotten. "Why, they sure enough did. Didn't Boo get herse'f a nice dawg to walk backn-forth from that school bus every day? Ain't she gwine have herse'f her own pet dawg fum now on?"

"That's right. Of course."

"An' didn't Mr. Tom and Miss Lisa find themse'fs a baby? This been a good week for me." Now she is smiling with her whole face, and chuckling and mutter-ing in that half-wordless way she does when she is right smart tickled.

"An' then this mawning, you got the letter, Missy," she says. She says it so softly I know that she knows all about it, the waiting and the worry—and the silence.

"But Lilliam, how did you know?"

"Nev' mind how," she says, still in the whisper. "I jes knowed."

She turns her back to me, so I need not have her looking into my face just now. She stirs something noisily in a bowl, and the kitchen is full of that cheerful sound.

"Yas'm. Mighty good week for me," she says above the clatter.

"But Lilliam ... those things didn't exactly happen to *you*, did they?"

She turns around quickly and looks at me in puzzlement, unable to imagine what I could possibly mean.

"Cose they happened to me," she says. "I seen 'em, didn't I?"

Those are the things that make a happy week for her ... wonderful things which she saw happen to other people. I want to get up and kiss her; I want to say, "Darling, never mind the letters ... you teach me, please." But that would embarrass us both.

So I only bend my head quickly, so she will not see the tears in my eyes, and the humility because we have been given this lamp for our house. I keep my head bent a moment while I wish that all the world, so hungry for happiness, so lost for it, could find one ray of that simple joy of hers, that abundance which counts her neighbors' happiness as if it were her own.

(3)